SHELDON

F

C000095906

DR E. STEWART JOHNSON is a pharmacologist and medical practitioner. He is presently the Medical Director of a pharmaceutical company. He belongs to the British Pharmacological Society, the Physiological Society, and the British Medical Association. He has held academic appointments in the Universities of Edinburgh and London; he is a Reader Emeritus in Pharmacology of the University of London. He is the former Hon. Research Director of the City of London Migraine Clinic, of which he remains a Trustee. He has written numerous papers and articles on various aspects of medicine, and has talked about feverfew on both television and radio. He is married with two children.

Overcoming Common Problems Series

For a full list of titles please contact
Sheldon Press, Marylebone Road, London NW1 4DU

Overcoming Common Problems

SHELDON NATURAL REMEDIES
FEVERFEW

Dr E. Stewart Johnson

sheldon PRESS

First published in Great Britain in 1997 by
Sheldon Press, SPCK, Marylebone Road, London NW1 4DU

British Library Cataloguing-in-Publication Data
A catalogue record for this book is available from the British Library

ISBN 0–85969–770–3

Photoset by Deltatype Ltd, Birkenhead, Merseyside
Printed in Great Britain by
Biddles Ltd, Guildford and King's Lynn

Contents

Acknowledgements

I am indebted to all those feverfew users and the scientists and doctors at King's College, London, and the City of London Migraine Clinic, whose cooperation made the series of clinical investigations discussed in the book possible. In particular, I would like to thank the joint Medical Directors of the City of London Migraine Clinic, Drs Marcia Wilkinson and Nat Blau, who generously gave both advice and encouragement throughout these investigations. Some of the expenses incurred by patients coming in to London to take part in the trials were borne by the British Migraine Association and the Association's support in this regard is greatly appreciated.

I also owe debts of gratitude to Margaret Skinner of the King's College Computer Centre, who computerized the feverfew results and was the source of endless statistical advice, and to Drs Deborah and Peter Hylands, formerly of Chelsea College (now King's College, London), who provided tablets and capsules for some of the clinical studies mentioned and prepared the extracts of feverfew for biological testing.

Finally, I am most grateful to the many people who have written to me over the years since my first book on feverfew was published.

Introduction

Feverfew has been used for centuries to treat headaches and other ailments, but, until relatively recently, it has not been taken seriously by scientists and researchers. This, however, is changing, following a resurgence in its use by ordinary people. They have spread the word, telling of their positive experiences. They pass on the news that they have become symptom-free as a result of taking feverfew, many of them having suffered from migraine for years, finding that conventional treatment has failed to bring them complete relief. The scientists are now, therefore, starting to look into why this plant seems to help where modern medicines cannot always.

This book looks at how this resurgence in the popularity of feverfew came about, how it can be beneficial for sufferers of migraine, arthritis and other conditions and what has so far been found out about how it works. Further, it offers guidance on how to recognize feverfew plants and propagate them, as well as dos and don'ts for choosing feverfew products.

Having all the available information to hand, you can then decide whether or not feverfew is likely to be able to help you and, if you do decide to take it, how to do so safely.

1

Migraine and its treatment

Most of us have the occasional headache and usually it is of so little consequence we don't even bother to see our doctor. Headaches seem inextricably linked with life itself, yet nobody seems to know why man suffers from them. In a few cases, they are the warning signs of more serious abnormalities within the skull, such as a growth, blood loss or infection, but probably the vast majority of severe headaches are due either to tension or migraine. Tension-type headache is so named because it results from the increased tension that occurs within the muscles of the scalp, neck and face; it often recurs day after day for weeks on end. Migraine is quite different.

What is migraine?

Migraine tends to run in families and is characteristically a severe headache – often on one side of the head only – that comes and goes, with days, weeks or even months of complete freedom between attacks. However, it is not simply a severe headache. To be diagnosed as migraine, it is generally accepted by doctors that this intermittent headache has to be associated with other symptoms, such as nausea, vomiting or diarrhoea. Before the headache proper begins, disturbances in the normal functioning of the nervous system may be experienced, such as visual symptoms, mood changes or numbness or weakness of an arm or leg on the opposite side of the body to the headache.

There are several kinds of migraine and the same person may experience different symptoms from attack to attack. Furthermore, no two people have attacks that are identical in form, frequency of occurrence, duration or severity, and it is often only when the attack rate or severity changes that the sufferer is prompted to seek medical advice.

One of the interesting things about migraine is that when the sufferer is examined, there does not appear to be anything physically wrong. As my former teacher – and perhaps the UK's most experienced migraine specialist – Dr Marcia Wilkinson always impressed on me, 'If you find anything wrong, it isn't migraine!'

In 1985, the International Headache Society formed a headache classification committee and it published the first international classification of all headache disorders in 1988. In it, there are 13 major groups, of which group 1 includes migraine variants and group 3 includes cluster headache.

There are two main types of migraine:

- migraine with aura (classical migraine)
- migraine without aura (common migraine).

Cluster headache is often included as a migraine variant as it has some of the features of migraine and some treatments for migraine can be used for cluster headache, too.

Migraine with aura

Before the headache, the sufferer experiences symptoms such as flashing lights, blurred sight, temporary partial loss of vision, geometric designs resembling fortifications expanding sideways from the centre of vision or even loss of speech. This stage – known as the *aura* – usually lasts only 15 to 20 minutes. As the visual symptoms lessen, the headache begins and then gradually increases in intensity. It has a throbbing character and, at its peak, is a very severe, nagging headache. During this time, the sufferer usually dislikes noise and being in daylight, preferring a quiet, darkened room. As the headache builds up, the sufferer feels sick and may even vomit, after which the pain sometimes eases.

Occasionally, the aura symptoms can occur on their own, without the headache.

Migraine without aura

This most frequently encountered form of migraine does not involve visual disturbances. The throbbing headache is often the first symptom to be noticed, and is just as severe as that of migraine with aura. The headache is aggravated by routine physical activity, and the sufferer has an increased sensitivity to noise and light. The headache is as likely as migraine with aura to be on one side only and usually each time it is on the same side of the head, though it may switch to the opposite side for no obvious reason. Nausea nearly always occurs and vomiting sometimes comes in addition or shortly after.

Migraine with and without aura are both more often suffered by women than men. Indeed, only a quarter to one third of all migraine sufferers are men.

Cluster headache

This much less common form of migraine differs from migraine with and without aura in that it usually affects men and only rarely women. The reason for this is not known.

Cluster headache usually affects one side of the head as in migraine but the attacks tend to occur in groups, or clusters, and these can last weeks or months, then suddenly disappear for several months or even years. The intensely painful headache comes on suddenly, lasts for one to one-and-a-half hours and may be at its most severe in, around or behind one eye, which waters and reddens. The nose feels 'stuffed up' on the affected side. The sufferer may experience more than one attack a day and they will usually occur on most days until, just as suddenly as they began, they cease.

At what age does it begin?

When 300 migraine sufferers who had taken or were taking the herb feverfew were asked how old they were when their migraines began, half said that they began before the age of 20 and more than a quarter said they began at or before the age of 12. Only one in ten said that attacks started after the age of 45.

This demonstrates one of the interesting characteristics of migraine: it usually begins at a young age. Any incidence of severe headache occurring for the first time in late middle age is taken very seriously as it is more likely then to be due to high blood pressure or some other condition requiring treatment and usually investigated in a hospital out-patient department.

Timing, duration and frequency

Doctors (quite rightly) tell their patients to take painkillers as soon as they detect the first symptoms of an impending attack. Unfortunately, this is often not possible because most migraine without aura sufferers wake up to find that their headache is already established and painkillers don't seem to work very well once the migraine has reached its peak. However, migraine attacks can occur at any time of day and some people find that the symptoms come on in the evening, just when they are beginning to relax after a hard day's work. Many sufferers report that attacks occur at weekends, when they tend to interfere with the whole family's leisure pursuits.

Some women suffer attacks regularly just before or during their monthly periods. Somewhat surprisingly, if they are taking the Pill and it contains the two artificial hormones oestrogen and progesto-gen, the migraine attacks occur more often in the Pill-free seven days. These observations and the commonly experienced remission during pregnancy and the menopause has meant that migraine has been linked with the way the hormones work in women.

In migraine with aura, the aura phase usually lasts only about a quarter of an hour, but the headache that follows may last anything from 4 to 72 hours, as in the case of migraine without aura. However, if antinauseants, painkillers or specific antimigraine drugs are taken very early in an attack (preferably when the first warning signs are experienced) or if the sufferer can go to sleep, its severity and duration are often curtailed.

Doctors feel uneasy about diagnosing migraine if the attacks occur more frequently than twice or three times a week as, by definition, migraine is an intermittent disorder with periods of complete normality between attacks. Except in cluster headache, migraine does not occur every day. Daily headaches are nearly always due to tension.

What is the cause?

No one has yet adequately explained the cause, or causes, of migraine. The throbbing, deep-seated pain, which is made worse by sudden movements such as standing upright after tying a shoelace, indicates that blood vessels inside the skull are involved. It is, in fact, known that blood vessels become narrower or wider during a migraine attack, but it is not easy to link these changes with the other symptoms that occur.

The aura of migraine usually involves visual symptoms, consisting of flashing lights, shimmering effects or partial loss of vision. These symptoms have their origin in the back of the brain (the visual cortex). When blood flow through this area has been measured while the patient is suffering the aura, it has been observed that it decreases, indicating that there is a narrowing of the blood vessels. If the narrowing is very marked, this can so reduce the blood supply that the brain doesn't receive enough oxygen to allow the brain cells to function normally. Some doctors believe that this accounts for the visual disturbances.

The back of the brain is not the only part to be affected. The side of the brain that controls speech, sensation and movement can also suffer a temporary reduction in its blood supply. When this is marked, speech may become slurred, one hand and arm may feel numb or tingle with pins and needles and, in a few instances, the sufferer may lose the ability to grip properly or even notice that they are dragging one foot rather than walking normally. All these symptoms last for only a few minutes then, for some reason, still not fully understood, the blood vessels widen, become very sensitive and, when this happens, the headache begins.

For several decades, researchers have been interested in what causes these blood vessel changes. They have looked at whether or not any chemical substances in the blood alter during the attack, which might account for the changes in blood flow to the brain, and have suggested that increases or decreases in certain natural substances called *amines* and *prostaglandins* might be responsible. This is because some blood vessels are known to narrow or widen in the presence of these substances. The chief amines thought to be responsible are serotonin and noradrenaline – mainly because some of the most effective treatments for migraine act on the specific sensitive sites or receptors that are usually stimulated by one or other of these amines.

As the levels of these substances may increase in stressful situations it is not surprising that migraine patients report that attacks often occur when they are under mental or physical stress. Thus, to modify the actions of these substances in the body to overcome the symptoms, stimulants or agonists and 'anti' drugs, or blockers, have been developed. The most important of these is the serotonin agonist sumatriptan (Imigran) – used in the treatment of severe acute migraine attacks. The noradrenaline blocker propranolol has been used for many years to prevent frequent migraines from occurring.

Prostaglandins are believed to be involved in the production of pain, whether this be the head pain of migraine or the joint pain of arthritis. Although no true antiprostaglandin drug has yet been

6

introduced for general use, drugs now known to be capable of preventing the formation of prostaglandins – aspirin for instance – have been in use for almost a century. It was largely British researchers, one of whom was awarded the Nobel Prize for Medicine in 1982, who discovered how aspirin works.

Does anything provoke a migraine attack?

When 300 migraine sufferers who were taking, or had taken, feverfew were asked whether anything in particular brought on a migraine attack, 83 per cent of them mentioned one or several of the following, which are given in order of the frequency with which they were mentioned by the sufferers:

- stress (anxiety and tension) 37.4%
- chocolate or cocoa 32.3%
- cheese and dairy products 28.1%
- alcohol 20.9%
- menstrual periods 18.9%
- overwork or exercise 17.4%
- citrus fruit 13.5%
- extreme climatic conditions (intense heat, heavy rain, snow) 11.5%
- bright or flickering light, TV 11.5%
- smoky/stuffy atmosphere 8.5%
- long journeys 8.0%
- fried foods 7.7%
- food preservatives (sodium nitrate), preserved foods 7.7%
- sudden loud noises, fright 7.2%
- strong odours, pleasant or otherwise 5.5%
- low blood sugar 5.5%
- relaxation 5.5%
- tea or coffee 5.1%
- onions 5.1%
- yeast extracts 3.8%
- getting up late 3.8%
- overeating 2.1%
- fish 2.1%
- sudden changes in posture 1.7%

- draughts 1.0%
- allergy 0.5%.

All of these are well known to doctors as precipitating, or 'trigger', factors and they broadly fall into four groups:

- *stress-related factors*, consisting of psychological (anger, anxiety, worry, elation, depression) and physical (overwork, exercise, long journeys) stress.
- *dietary triggers*, comprising foods (such as chocolate, cocoa, oranges, chips, onions, fish, yeast extracts, tea, coffee), alcoholic drinks, especially wines and going without meals (low blood sugar).
- *hormonal factors*, such as menstruation and the Pill.
- *environmental factors*, such as extremes of climatic conditions, bright light, flicker (fluorescent lights and TV, cinema), loud noises, smoky or stuffy atmospheres, strong odours and so on.

As a result of the pioneering work of the British doctor Edda Hanington, we now have a very plausible explanation as to why certain foodstuffs trigger migraine attacks. They contain large amounts of amines that are chemically similar to those produced in the body when a person is under stress or experiencing a migraine attack (see page 6). Migraine sufferers seem to be particularly sensitive to these dietary amines.

For detailed discussion of migraine-precipitating factors, I suggest you read the excellent accounts given in Dr Marcia Wilkinson's book *Living with Migraine* and *Migraine*, edited by Dr J. N. Blau.

The standard treatments for migraine

Avoidance of triggers

If there is a recognizable dietary trigger, say, or an activity that provokes an attack, this should be avoided wherever possible. Of course, it isn't always practicable to avoid every trigger, but they can be kept to a minimum. Some migraine sufferers go to the extreme of avoiding all foods believed to trigger migraine, but this makes life difficult. In my view, sufferers should never avoid a particular foodstuff permanently, unless they are absolutely certain that it provokes their attacks.

The standard treatments for acute attacks

The sufferer who experiences only two or three migraine attacks a year often requires only simple painkillers, such as aspirin or paracetamol, to cope with symptoms. If nausea and vomiting are a problem, then an antisickness medication, such as metoclopramide (Maxolon or Primperan) or prochlorperazine (Stemetil) is also prescribed, and should be taken as soon as the first symptom of an impending attack is noted. In cases where taking pills or tablets makes the sufferer more likely to vomit, the medication can be given as suppositories.

If the migraine does not respond to simple painkillers, more powerful drugs such as sumatriptan or ergotamine may be prescribed. The disadvantage of ergotamine is that it can produce serious side-effects if the stated dose is exceeded.

If psychological stress is an obvious trigger, sedatives may be prescribed. Sleep is part of the recovery process and so the preferred sedatives are those which enable the patient to get off to sleep without subsequently causing persistent muzziness. Temazepam is a useful medicine in this situation, as it remains in the body for only a short time.

Prevention with drugs

When patients suffer more than two attacks every month, drugs which are antiserotonin in action, such as pizotifen, or antinoradrenaline in action, such as propranolol, may be prescribed to prevent attacks. The trouble is that, although they are of benefit to many, people often find that it is very difficult to stick to taking them every day. Furthermore, a significant minority experiences side-effects when taking these drugs.

Whenever migraine is tackled with a new preventive treatment, a proportion of sufferers experiences a marked improvement for two to three months, then the attacks return to their previous frequency, severity and duration. These people, whose hopes had been raised initially, will therefore ask to be taken off the tablets. Such an initial favourable response to treatment is common – perhaps as high as 35 per cent, especially if the patient is taking part in a clinical trial of a new medicine. This is known as a placebo response (from the Latin placebo, meaning 'I shall please'). For this reason, it is essential to compare a new drug with a dummy (placebo) to make sure that the initial placebo effect is not wrongly credited to the action of the new drug but it is actually having a positive effect, not working or whatever is the case.

Scope for improvement

Migraine is one of the commonest conditions afflicting mankind. In terms of frequency of occurrence, it is probably equivalent to high blood pressure. Migraine is therefore one of the medical conditions pharmaceutical companies focus on with a view to improving on their existing products. One significant pharmacological break-through in the treatment of migraine has been the drug sumatriptan (Imigran), which has been a godsend to some sufferers.

Side-effects of antimigraine drugs

Some improvements have been made in antimigraine treatments – side-effects, for instance, have been lessened – but there is still much scope for improvement.

Self-help and the last hope

There are a great many ways in which migraine sufferers can help themselves. Learning to relax, avoiding trigger factors (see page 8), finding the painkiller that suits them best and lying down in a quiet, darkened room are some of them. However, judging from the correspondence I have received, going to see the doctor is often not high on the list. This may be because sufferers seldom feel well enough to see their doctors while they are having a migraine attack and when they are better there seems to be no reason to trouble them. The last thing a sufferer wants to do during an attack, of course, is to make an appointment and have to drive or walk to the surgery. Also, being aware that their condition is only temporary and that they will be back to normal in a day or so, makes them tend not to request a home visit from their doctor.

A recent survey by a major drug company showed that some four out of every five migraine sufferers buy expensive 'over the counter' proprietary medicines to help them cope with their condition. Bearing in mind that an estimated eighth of the adult population suffers from migraine, this is self-medication on a very large scale indeed.

Does it perhaps indicate a lack of confidence on the part of some sufferers in the more migraine-specific drug treatments, such as those containing ergotamine, previously prescribed by their doctor? This may be so, but doctors know only too well that many migraine sufferers who claim that a treatment does not work have not taken the medicine in either the correct dose or, more importantly, at the correct time – that is, with the onset of the first symptoms of an impending attack. However, there are undoubtedly sufferers who, not having had any success with treatments obtained from their doctors, will try anything and everything the chemist has to offer. This can be very expensive and, perhaps, futile.

There are migraine sufferers who have tried nearly all of the available specific antimigraine drugs and preventives prescribed, taking them as directed and complying with the treatment in every way, often for many years. They have visited specialist migraine clinics and yet have gained no significant relief or the drugs prescribed have caused unacceptable side-effects. Among these are women whose attacks seem to be linked with their menstrual cycle, occurring just before or on the first day of their periods. Some find that the only time they do not suffer from migraine is when they are pregnant. Such sufferers can be so seriously disabled during an attack that they will try anything and eventually try feverfew. A typical example is that of a housewife who writes:

> I have been a severe migraine sufferer since the age of eight years and have tried various treatments which made me vomit so much that I developed hiatus hernia. I am now unable to use any form of treatment containing the drug ergotamine as I developed side-effects, e.g. loss of feeling in toes and fingers and severe pain in the limbs. As you can imagine, I was more than pleased to read any information about cures for migraine. A friend found feverfew growing in a hedge. I started taking the leaf every day . . . I have since had no attacks until yesterday but . . . no vomiting took place . . . To be free from an attack of migraine is marvellous as I had one at least every week.

Another sufferer, who obtained only partial relief from aspirin or paracetamol, writes:

> Since adolescence I had suffered migraine headaches on a more or less permanent basis, each headache lasting three to four days

with only a day or two break before the next one. The only relief I got was from taking aspirin or paracetamol, the two having to be alternated at varying intervals as I seemed to get used to them after a while. I think on average I used to get through 40 to 50 tablets per week!

When I read about feverfew I really thought no more than 'Oh well, I'll try anything once'. I knew when I started the leaves that the effects were not instant and would take anything up to six months to become fully effective, so perseverance was the key word, especially as I found the leaves disgusting to eat. Anyway, after two or three weeks I did notice my headaches were possibly lessening, but I used to get fleeting 'twinges' to remind me of what it used to be like. After about three months my misery had almost completely disappeared, and now I just keep taking my daily feverfew to live a normal life.

A 60-year-old woman who had suffered two to three migraine attacks a week since childhood began taking two leaves of feverfew daily in June 1971 and five months later she wrote:

Since then I have experienced only one very minor migraine attack. All through my school life and right until the beginning of July this year, at least one day a week was sheer misery.

It was press reports of case histories such as these and the gradual realization that feverfew leaves were being eaten in seemingly epidemic proportions that caught my attention. What struck me most was that this treatment seemed still to be working months or even years after sufferers first started eating the leaves, but was this so?

Late one autumn I chanced to see three patients at the City of London Migraine Clinic who gave me this same story, which I was coming to know so well – that of a long history of migraine, suffering from childhood, which had not responded to conventional preventive drugs, then giving feverfew a try, not believing for a minute that it would work, yet it had.

I remember being impressed by the beneficial changes in the lives of these three patients and mildly embarrassed by the fact that it was not the treatments I had prescribed for them that had brought about these improvements. They seemed grateful to me, despite the fact that they had apparently found their salvation for themselves. Also, I distinctly recall that after seeing the first patient, I was sceptical and wondered, rather uncharitably, whether she might be a little eccentric. After all, who in their right minds would eat garden weeds?! In the chapters that follow we shall see how my scepticism was partly overcome and why feverfew seems to be beneficial for so many people.

2

The Welsh connection

The suggestion that feverfew might be of value in the prevention of migraine came in 1978 and 1979 when several articles appeared in the national and provincial press.

An investigatory article in the health magazine *Prevention* reported the 'simple success story of a little weed' that had the power to cure classical migraine completely and, as a bonus, relieve, if not reverse, advanced arthritic conditions. The article recounted the story of Mrs Ann Jenkins, a 68-year-old Cardiff doctor's wife, who had suffered migraine since she was 16. An unusual feature of her migraine attacks was that they increased in frequency in middle age, so that by the age of 50 they were occurring at least every ten days and lasted for two or three days. She tried treatment after treatment, but to no avail and medicines containing ergotamine made her vomit.

In 1973, a friend of Mrs Jenkins' sister mentioned Mrs Jenkins' plight to her elderly father. He had found feverfew effective in treating arthritis and suggested to Mrs Jenkins that it might be useful for migraine also. He sent her a plant with the advice that every day she should take a 'pinch' of fresh leaf.

In 1974, Mrs Jenkins decided to take a whole small leaf every day, 'chopped, in a bread and butter sandwich'. When nothing happened, she increased the dose to three small leaves. Day after day she persevered and very little happened for five months. Then, although the headaches persisted, the vomiting associated with the migraine stopped. She also found that she was using her Medihaler ergotamine less and less. After six months, she went for a whole month without a headache. The occasional 'breakthrough' headache occurred until the tenth month, after which time she had no further attacks.

She told no one that she was taking the plant until she had convinced herself that it was helping. Then, she gave the plant to equally desperate migraine sufferers – some 15 in all by 1978 – with similar results.

Mrs Jenkins' story is typical of the migraine sufferer who turns to feverfew. The benefits she experienced, with no side-effects, after so many years of unsatisfactory orthodox treatment, led her to advocate it enthusiastically to others in the same predicament.

A summary of the account in *Prevention* was written up for the *Sunday Express* by Robert Chapman, a science correspondent, and published 21 May 1978. For this account, the views of the London-based Migraine Trust were sought and the then Director of the Trust, Derek Mullis, was quoted as saying: 'We are always hearing of unusual treatments for migraine, but few seem to remain effective for long. The use of feverfew is certainly interesting. I shall be making further enquiries about it.'

And he did. He got in touch with me at King's College and we discussed the possibility of looking into the chemical constituents of the plant. I did not take things any further for a few months, but Mr Mullis continued to pass on to me any interesting correspondence received by the Migraine Trust from feverfew users.

The articles about Mrs Jenkins had also mentioned the alleviation of her symptoms of arthritis, for which purpose feverfew was used as long ago as the sixteenth century. According to John Gerarde, the writer of *The Herball* or *General Historie of Plantes* in 1597, it was 'profitable applied to Saint Antonies fire, to all inflammation and hot swellings'.

Mrs Jenkins' 'discovery' continued to be covered in the media through to late in the summer of 1978 with a television interview and her story being told once more by Grafton Radcliffe of the *Glamorgan Gazette* in August. This coverage stimulated a great deal of interest among migraine and arthritis sufferers and hundreds of people contacted Mrs Jenkins for further information or with requests for feverfew plants or seeds. Mrs Jenkins produced a leaflet showing the amount in small or large leaves she took each day and giving general information on its cultivation. Hundreds of sufferers followed her example and many claimed that it had benefited them and were truly grateful.

The Migraine Trust was occasionally chided for not acknowledging the importance of this discovery, as did this correspondent in August 1979:

I have now been taking feverfew for one year, and it is like a miracle to me ... I have many friends who have also benefited and who feel as I do that a very big 'thank you' is due to Mrs Jenkins – and why not through the Migraine Trust.

Another sufferer who was greatly helped by Mrs Jenkins' treatment regimen wrote to the Trust:

> I wish someone could do some research into this plant to see if it could, in the long run, have any side-effects. As far as I am concerned now, I could not be more grateful for the valuable information Mrs Jenkins has given. Once again after more than 20 years I can lead a normal life.

In the media, the news about feverfew was all good. In *Farmers Weekly*, Paul Lees wrote an enthusiastic account about a retired farmer – Herbert Swann of Great Totham, Essex – who, although not a migraine sufferer himself, grew the plant and dispatched it both fresh and dried all over the world. Mr Swann and his wife Christine had previously featured in the newsletter of the British Migraine Association, after which he was inundated with letters requesting plants. Professional herb growers, however, were not quick to respond to the demand.

The article in *Farmers Weekly* carried a statement by the then Honorary Secretary of the British Migraine Association, Peter Wilson, who said that the Association had been particularly interested in feverfew but that one or two people had experienced difficulties with it: 'We have had a few complaints that the user has reacted with blisters in the mouth and throat'.

Mr Wilson pointed out that the Association was interested in the possible testing of another herbal remedy for migraine, devil's claw, but that '. . . we don't take these remedies too seriously in view of the highly likely placebo effect'.

These comments illustrate the dilemma faced by the migraine charities. While the public was reading about the advantages of feverfew, the charities were also receiving many letters from those who found that the plant did not suit them:

> I only took feverfew for about two weeks. Ulcers began to form in my mouth and I was afraid of being ill . . .

> She only took feverfew for about six weeks and then had a very intense allergic reaction to it – her mouth and lips swelled as though stung. She has not taken any since.

... She never received any benefit whatsoever from taking the feverfew, and eventually gave the whole thing a miss saying it was rubbish and that she had no confidence whatsoever in its so-called medicinal properties.

In fact, over the four months the feverfew did not make any difference.

We were disappointed when the feverfew sandwiches did not help.

However, after taking half the suggested amount of two tea-spoonsful of the granules (chrysanthemum and sugar crystals, sold as feverfew) dissolved in water, I experienced severe heart 'pumping' which was both distressing and frightening.

After about six migraine-free weeks my mouth and throat became so severely swollen that I could hardly manage to eat or drink ...

So, the charities could hardly be blamed for not joining with the popular press in extolling the virtues of feverfew.

Then came a further development. In June 1979, a surgeon writing in *Woman's Weekly* under the pen-name 'Doctor Margaret', alleged that feverfew could damage the liver. Readers had asked whether or not there were any dangers in using herbal remedies rather than artificially produced drugs, and Doctor Margaret replied:

Yes, herbal remedies can, in some cases, be dangerous. They are not pure substances and most of them have not been completely analysed. Some – feverfew, for instance – contain quite potent liver poisons, which have caused illness, sometimes very serious.

If you are taking other medicines, those may react disastrously with some of the herbal constituents. It is true that herbal treatment is satisfactory in a number of cases, but self-medication can be dangerous and you should ask your doctor whether he is happy for you to use herbs before you dose yourself with them.

As a matter of fact, little was known about the effects of feverfew on liver function in June 1979 and it was rather a strange example to use when there were so many other herbs that were known to harm the liver that she could have mentioned to serve her purpose.

The article had an immediate and alarming effect on those taking feverfew, many of whom stopped taking it. This proved useful to me, as I wanted to know what happened when people stopped taking the plant, but it wasn't an experience enjoyed by those who stopped. As far as I was able to ascertain, a little over half of those who were taking feverfew in June 1979, stopped doing so as a result of reading, or hearing about the article in *Woman's Weekly*.

Typical of the letters received by the Migraine Trust was that from a housewife in Matlock, written in July 1979, soon after Doctor Margaret's article appeared:

> About a year ago I was recommended the 'weed' feverfew as a cure for migraine. To my delight it really worked, reducing attacks from at least two a week to one now and again, and the attacks I did have were not as acute and easily dismissed.
>
> However, I read in a magazine recently that this weed, if eaten, could cause liver damage so I have ceased eating the three leaves a day. Now my migraines have returned to two a week.
>
> The tablets Migraleve sometimes help me, but not to the same extent that eating the leaves of feverfew did. I wondered if you could clarify this situation for me and tell me if feverfew really does cause liver or any other damage.

Even doctors enquired in this vein on behalf of their patients.

Clearly such letters had to be answered. I wanted to be reassuring, I just did not know whether or not the plant was indeed harmful. So my standard reply admitted my lack of knowledge on feverfew's efficacy and safety, but also included a summary of what was known about side-effects and the opinion that, until more was known about it, feverfew could not be recommended. My typical reply to a query from a doctor was therefore:

> Feverfew (*Chrysanthemum parthenium*) is used by many migraine and arthritis sufferers to prevent attacks. Its pharmacology and toxicology are largely unknown, but liver function tests of the few patients we have assessed have been normal. Adverse effects include severe mouth ulceration, palpitations, epigastric discomfort and fleeting muscle pains on discontinuation. Its long-term effects are unknown and we cannot therefore recommend its use at the present time.

This essentially remained my view until January 1983, when, as the liver function and other blood tests of feverfew users were consistently normal, I felt confident enough to then not discourage patients from taking the plant.

By September 1978, however, it had become apparent that the eating of feverfew was widespread and represented a potential public health problem if, by chance, it should turn out to be harmful. On 28 October 1978, the *British Medical Journal* published what was then known of the scientific evidence to support the use of feverfew in the prevention of recurrent attacks of migraine. What was known was incomplete and mostly wrong, but this small article showed the degree of awareness by doctors of the lay use of feverfew.

In my earlier discussions with Derek Mullis, Director of the Migraine Trust, I had explained that a research project based simply on anecdotal newspaper reports was not on. Nothing would be wasted, however, were we to identify a reliable source of plants just in case I changed my mind. Soon afterwards, one of my students located a large quantity of them growing in the gardens of King's College's own Plant Sciences Department in South London.

Such a highly speculative project as the testing for biological activity of feverfew leaves was low on my list of priorities. The Migraine Trust gave the college a small donation to cover part of the cost, but it would have been hugely costly to set up a research programme to identify the active compounds. The project was therefore given as an exercise to an undergraduate student reading for a B.Sc. degree in Pharmacology. Although his studies were based on very crude extracts, they indicated that feverfew did indeed have some actions that might be worth following up. By coincidence, the idea of a chemical extraction programme had occurred simultaneously to Dr Peter Hylands, a lecturer in pharmacognosy (the science of drugs derived from natural sources) at Chelsea College. He had been following the newspaper reports of feverfew and, along with his PhD student, Deborah Jessup (later to become Mrs Hylands), the three of us formed a research partnership.

In Welsh literature

The treatment of severe headache and probably migraine with feverfew is not new. In 1707, J. Pechey in his *Compleat Herbal of Physical Plants*, wrote: 'Take of feverfew one handful, warm it in a frying pan, apply it twice or thrice hot; this cures a hemicrania [that is, migraine]: And the crude herb applied to the top of the head, cures the headache.' What is new, however, is its rediscovery and oral use as a preventive treatment almost three centuries later entirely by individual people, not medically trained, who have passed on the information from one to another following press accounts of Mrs Jenkins' observations.

It seems particularly appropriate, therefore, that the connection of feverfew and headache can be traced back through the centuries in Welsh literature and I am particularly grateful to Dr G. Wynne Griffith of Beaumaris for his translation from the Welsh of this Appendix to a book entitled *A Welsh Botanology, Part the First: A systematic Catalogue of the native plants of the Isle of Anglesey*, published in 1813 by Hugh Davies:

Wermod Wen: Pyrethrum Parthenium; Common Feverfew
This common, innocent herb possesses medicinal properties beyond praise, and of great value in relation to women: there is no drug used by physicians as effective in easing and bringing on the periods, nor for all kinds of maternal disorders. It also is beneficial for the bowels, against worms, and the intermittent fever. Having made a strong infusion of the leaves with boiling water, the patient should drink about half a pint twice or thrice a day. A virtuous gentlewoman who had suffered greatly for a long time, so much so that in her youth she was driven almost insane at times with terrible headaches, frequently recurring, and having spent much money on physicians, to no use or profit whatsoever, in time was completely cured by this means: she drank copiously of the infusion of the leaves, and made a plaster or warm compress of the leaves from which the infusion had been made, to place on that part of the head where the headache was: the disease left her never to return.

Obviously, the popularity of feverfew as a treatment was growing rapidly, but major questions remained unanswered. Did it really

20

work? Could evidence be acquired that would satisfy the most sceptical of medical scientists? Was it working by suggestion in severely afflicted people willing to grasp any straw? Was it safe to take? It seemed to me that the first step was to contact as many feverfew users as possible and to discover what proportion had apparently gained some benefit from long-term use.

3

Does feverfew work?

It was obvious from the beginning that there would be no point in expending a great deal of effort and money on laboratory testing unless I had more reliable information on the effectiveness of feverfew in migraine than merely anecdotal press reports. So my wife, Dr Trilby Johnson, and I compiled a comprehensive questionnaire to be distributed to as many long-term feverfew users as we could find. It was to be restricted to those taking the plant for the prevention of migraine, and included questions on the parts of the plant eaten, how much, how they took it and for how long, the side-effects encountered and what happened when they stopped taking it.

The day after we compiled the questionnaire, I received a telephone call from a general practitioner in Kent, Dr John Gledhill who had heard about it from Mrs Jenkins. He had undertaken an open study of feverfew leaves on his own patients and felt certain there were grounds for believing that it worked. He had contacted a major pharmaceutical company and had been interviewed by one of its scientists, but had heard no more. Dr Gledhill agreed to distribute the questionnaire to his patients. The feverfew users who were my patients at the City of London Migraine Clinic and those provided by Dr Gledhill gave me 45 to 50 completed questionnaires. Then I remembered the offer made by Mrs Jenkins to the Migraine Trust in a letter dated 2 November 1978:

> Should any independent authoritative body wish to undertake an epidemiological survey on the use and value of this herb, I would, with the consent of the persons concerned be ready to supply names and addresses.

I wrote to her and she kindly sent me over 700 names and addresses.

Of all the people contacted, we heard from a little over a half, but many had taken feverfew for arthritis or had not taken it at all, some had originally enquired on behalf of others and 13 had died in the meantime. In due course, others heard about the questionnaire or wrote to the clinic about their own experiences with feverfew, so that many more completed forms were eventually received. They

22

were returned by individuals living as far apart as Penzance in south-west Cornwall and Elgin in the north of Scotland.

Characteristics of feverfew users

The ratio of women to men users was 5.3 to 1, their average ages were 55 and 54 years respectively and the information they provided showed that 88 per cent were suffering true migraine attacks. A further 8 per cent suffered from daily (tension) headache prior to taking feverfew.

In 50 per cent, the attacks had begun before they had reached 20 years of age and in 75 per cent this had happened by the age of 30. Their trigger factors resembled those reported in other surveys of migraine sufferers (see pages 7–8). In fact, these feverfew users resembled other migraine patients in every respect but one – their headaches had tended not to have responded to conventional medication. However, this problem had occurred before the intro-duction of sumatriptan.

Nearly 80 per cent of respondents said that they had learned of the plant from reports in newspapers or magazines. This underlines the influence of the popular press – nearly all of these people were prepared to take the plant every day without seeking medical advice as to the wisdom of it. At that time, with the one exception noted on page 17, no newspaper or magazine had suggested that the plant might be anything other than a harmless 'natural' cure, free of unwanted side-effects – the implication then being that feverfew is a herb, not a drug and only drugs have side-effects. The fact is, however, that once a herb is used as a medicine, it becomes, by definition, a drug. Only one in eight users had not started taking feverfew as a result of reading about it in the press. Among this group were individuals who learned of the plant by word of mouth.

The source and varieties

The majority of users (88 per cent) grew their own feverfew plants or obtained them from the garden of a friend or relative. There was considerable variation in the shape of the leaves consumed and it was obvious that several varieties were being used. However, the shapes of feverfew leaves may vary depending on the age of plants as well as by variety. They all have the characteristic camphor-like odour, though, which, as far as the medicinal properties of the plant are concerned, possibly has more significance than does the shape of the leaves.

Leaf colour is not an accurate indication of the variety of feverfew either. For example, root cuttings of wild feverfew planted out in soil rapidly yellow, whereas those from the same plants kept in a cold greenhouse in permanently wet soil remain green.

What part of the plant is eaten and what is the 'dose'?

Of all users, 92 per cent ate the leaves and 7 per cent also ate the soft stems of new growth with the leaves. If the plant is allowed to bolt into flower, it produces far more stem than leaves, so the flowering shoots should be nipped out early to encourage leaf growth. However, I have come across five users who ate not only the leaves and stems but flowers too, when in bloom.

The vast majority of feverfew users eat the plant freshly picked, although many long-term users have found that the dried leaf works just as well, and, as discussed in Chapter 5, the dried leaf is more convenient to take on holiday and in the winter.

Five out of six people take the leaves with food, water or both. Of those who take it without the assistance of these, some actually like the bitter flavour.

As a rule, feverfew is taken once every day, but there is no preferred time. The 'dose' taken varies considerably, because of the marked variability in the size and shape of leaves of different varieties of plants and plants of different ages. When the leaf dose was standardized into 'small leaf units' (those leaves 3.8 cm/1.5 inches long by 3.2 cm/1.25 inches wide), it was found that the average consumption was just over two-and-a-half leaves every day.

Are feverfew users more likely to use herbs than conventional medicines?

The answer to this is a decisive 'no'. Of all users, 75 per cent had never taken any other herbal remedies, and of those who said that they had, many had actually taken vitamin preparations bought over the counter, which couldn't be classed as herbal products. In fact, nearly all sufferers had taken medicines prescribed by their family doctors. For example, 75 per cent had taken ergotamine at some time or other, a drug usually only prescribed when patients fail to respond to simple painkillers.

Just under half (about 45 per cent) of respondents had found the common painkillers aspirin and paracetamol to be of any help. However, two other treatments used for treating the symptoms of migraine attacks had been relatively successful for a greater proportion of people. The first of these was Migraleve, available on prescription or over the counter at chemists. Migraleve combats nausea as well as being a painkiller. Those who found Migraleve to be effective were also more likely to continue to use it. The second was ergotamine, which appeared to be as effective as Migraleve. However, when feverfew was taken, users tended to stop taking ergotamine twice as often as Migraleve. This almost certainly was because more people experienced side-effects with ergotamine than they did with Migraleve. Also, ergotamine cannot be obtained without a prescription.

Comparatively few people found preventive medicines, which had to be taken every day prior to the use of feverfew, to be of any help. Of those who had found them satisfactory, 66 per cent found that they were no longer necessary once they started taking feverfew. Clonidine (Dixarit), the preventive drug most commonly tried by feverfew users at some time or other, was found to be ineffective by 72 per cent of respondents.

The general response to feverfew

The questionnaire asked users whether their headaches while they were taking feverfew were less frequent, more frequent, less painful, more painful or unchanged. Of the 300 respondents 7.5 per cent were suffering from daily tension headache and not migraine, a further 6.6 per cent were taking conventional medicines used to prevent migraine attacks from occurring. This left for analysis 253 sets of results from people who apparently suffered a true migraine. Of these, 72 per cent claimed that their headaches were less frequent, less painful or both, 26 per cent thought they were unchanged and 2 per cent considered that their headaches worsened while they were taking feverfew.

We also wanted to learn how other types of headache responded to feverfew, so the replies from the 7.5 per cent of people who were suffering from tension headache were analysed separately. Of this small group, 78 per cent credited their reduction in headache frequency and severity to feverfew.

It is well known in medicine that common conditions commonly occur together, so we felt it was particularly important to ask all of the feverfew-using migraine sufferers whether they suffered from any other illness. In fact, 47 per cent said they did and the illnesses they had are as follows:

- allergy (including asthma, hayfever, angioneurotic oedema)
- anaemia
- angina
- atherosclerosis
- anxiety
- cataract
- chronic bronchitis
- cystitis
- depression
- diabetes (mild)
- diverticulitis, diverticulosis
- epilepsy
- fluid retention
- gout
- hiatus hernia, indigestion with acid reflux, nervous stomach, nausea and vomiting
- hypertension
- insomnia
- intestinal hurry, irritable bowel
- mastoiditis
- menopausal symptoms
- myxoedema (post-thyroidectomy)
- osteoarthritis (including slipped disc, sciatica, back pain, cervical spondylosis)
- palpitations
- peptic ulcer
- psoriasis
- pyelonephritis (kidney infection)
- rheumatoid arthritis

- sarcoidosis
- sinusitis, catarrh
- stomach abscess
- thrush, vaginal infection
- ulcerative colitis, colitis
- vertigo.

We also wanted to know whether the presence of another illness or its treatment might have influenced the high response rate, so my colleague from the King's College Computer Centre Miss Margaret Skinner and I analysed separately the data for those migraine sufferers who were not suffering from any other condition or taking any treatment likely to confuse the evaluation of feverfew in combating migraine. In this group, 72 per cent claimed that their headaches were less frequent, less painful or both as a result of taking feverfew, while 24 per cent thought they were unchanged as a result and 2 per cent were made worse by taking feverfew.

Thus, the success rate reported by those not suffering from any other illness or taking any other treatments was virtually identical to the success rate of those with other conditions for which additional medicines were being taken. There was, therefore, no reason to believe that feverfew has been credited with successful responses that were actually brought about by other drugs that patients happened to be taking at the same time.

The second way in which we assessed how beneficial feverfew had been for those who had taken it was to note down the actual numbers of attacks they had had each month before they took it and during. This was done for 242 respondents. It was found that 33 per cent of them had not had any migraine attacks at all while taking feverfew and, overall, some 76 per cent experienced fewer migraines each month than before they took the leaves. Thus, the two methods of assessing the effectiveness of feverfew on migraine yielded almost identical results.

Many of those who completed the questionnaires were subsequently invited to attend the City of London Migraine Clinic, where their case histories were studied in more detail. Three interesting additional facts emerged. First, those who, prior to taking feverfew, had suffered from nausea and vomiting during the headache phase, reported that they no longer vomited and seldom felt sick since they started taking it. Second, when they did get a migraine, it tended to respond more readily to simple painkillers and was less likely to incapacitate them than before. Third, a proportion of those who suffered migraine with aura occasionally experienced the aura but no headache. Although this separation of migraine symptoms is not unknown to migraine specialists, it was interesting to find that feverfew seemed capable of influencing the course of an attack in this way.

The beneficial effects of most medicines often depend on the amount taken. For example, someone prescribed drug treatment for high blood pressure is often told that they might have to increase the dose if the response to the initial amount is inadequate. What constitutes the correct quantity of feverfew leaves to induce an optimal inhibition of migraine attacks has never been determined. Nor has it been established whether a person is more likely to experience side-effects if they take five leaves than if they take just one leaf a day.

The response to feverfew of migraine sufferers who also have other conditions

We thought it might be possible for migraine sufferers who also had another disease or illness to be less likely to respond to feverfew. So, a separate analysis was made of those suffering from each of the six most common additional conditions. These included allergic conditions (such as asthma and hayfever), anxiety and depression, high blood pressure, osteoarthritic disorders (including a slipped disc and cervical spondylosis), a variety of stomach disorders (such as peptic ulcers and hiatus hernia) and rheumatoid arthritis. With the possible exception of allergic disorders, an additional illness did not seem to affect how well feverfew worked for sufferers.

Is the benefit psychological?

It is known that many illnesses seem to respond to suggestion, and this is called the placebo response. This means that improvement is due to the fact that the patients gain relief from sharing their problems with the doctor or being given some treatment even when there is no active ingredient in it. Usually the beneficial placebo response does not last long and migraine attacks tend to return to

28

their pretreatment level after eight to 12 weeks. Sufferers also discover this effect when they try proprietary medicines as initially they seem to help, but later they do not.

Those who take feverfew have usually tried everything else that is available and have found that nothing works to their satisfaction. Thus, they are the least likely to elicit a placebo response as everything else has failed. They are also usually very surprised when they find that feverfew has helped them. Some were so anxious not to lose their newly found freedom from migraine that they flatly refused to participate in a clinical trial in case they were given a dummy (placebo) medication rather than feverfew and thus risk a recurrence of their attacks.

Two particular observations strongly suggest that the beneficial effect of feverfew cannot be attributed entirely to a placebo effect. First, the benefit lasts for as long as the individual takes the leaves. The average duration of treatment is 2.3 years for men and 2.6 years for women and I know of no placebo effect that lasts for this length of time. Second, when a sufferer who has experienced relief from symptoms suddenly stops taking the leaves, the attacks recur with their former frequency and severity, even, in some cases, after four or five years of continuous treatment. That this happens when the patient has no knowledge that the treatment has changed is evident from the results of clinical trials.

Clinical trials of feverfew as a treatment for migraine

Two double-blind clinical trials – that is, those in which neither doctor nor patient knows the identity of the treatment that the patient is receiving – with migraine sufferers have been completed since 1984.

The first trial, published in 1985 in the *British Medical Journal*, was carried out at the City of London Migraine Clinic. A total of 17 sufferers were enrolled who had been treating themselves with raw feverfew leaves every day for at least three months. All those taking part suffered from migraine with or without aura. The intention was to switch the patients from raw leaves to either feverfew powder in capsules or dummy (placebo) capsules. Eight patients received capsules containing freeze-dried feverfew powder and nine received identical-looking placebo capsules. The two groups had consumed similar daily amounts of feverfew prior to the study and for similar lengths of time.

The results of the study showed that those who received placebo capsules experienced a significant increase in the frequency and severity of headache, nausea and vomiting. The group given capsules of feverfew powder showed no change in the frequency or severity of their migraine symptoms.

Abruptly discontinuing feverfew after several years of use led to the recurrence of incapacitating migraine and, indeed, two of the sufferers who were being given the placebo were unable to complete the study because of this. Once they started taking raw feverfew again, this controlled their symptoms once more. Overall, unwanted effects were reported to a much greater extent by those taking the placebo than by those taking the feverfew.

Although this small 'pilot' trial appeared to give a clear-cut result that the feverfew herb can help migraine sufferers, its design was deliberately unusual. This was the first time that orthodox clinical evaluation of feverfew had been attempted and we had to address the possible ethical objection of giving those taking part a treatment that had been incompletely tested in animals. We therefore chose to include only those who were already taking the leaves. However, this left the study open to the criticism that these self-selected users of feverfew might have experienced a different response to the herb than might be seen in other migraine sufferers who had never taken it.

There was therefore the need to do a confirmatory study, preferably with a tablet or capsule of feverfew controlled for chemical content, of migraine sufferers who had never treated themselves with this herb. The results of such a study, carried out at the Department of Medicine, Nottingham University, were published in the *Lancet* in 1988.

This study was again double-blind and the 76 sufferers who took part suffered from migraine with or without aura. After a period of one month's assessment of their migraine while taking placebo capsules, the patients were randomly assigned to receive either one capsule of feverfew or a matching placebo capsule daily for four months. After this time, the participants swapped treatments and took these for four more months. Each capsule contained, on average, 82 mg of powder.

There was a significant 24 per cent reduction in the number of migraine episodes experienced by those receiving the feverfew treatment and the remaining headaches tended to be milder. Also, confirming the findings of the first study, there was a significant reduction in nausea and vomiting with each attack.

So, the finding that feverfew was of benefit to those using it long term was confirmed by the other migraine sufferers taking part in a conventional clinical trial. Feverfew did work to prevent migraine attacks from occurring.

The compatibility of feverfew with other medicines

In the studies, many different drugs were taken simultaneously with feverfew, sometimes for long periods. There was no evidence that feverfew reacted adversely with these medicines or that it neutralized their effects.

Similarly, the menstrual cycle was not upset in women taking both feverfew and the Pill and there was no reason to believe that feverfew reduced the ability of the Pill to protect against pregnancy.

Do the beneficial effects last?

The benefits certainly seem to last, but it is important to bear in mind that feverfew might only be suppressing the symptoms, not curing the condition itself. When individuals stop taking feverfew, their migraine returns – often within one week – and is usually as severe as it was before treatment with the plant was started. If feverfew consumption is resumed, the attacks disappear again. The curious fact is that, in such cases, they are controlled almost at once whereas when these same people initially started taking feverfew, several weeks or months usually passed before the frequency of attacks was reduced or the attacks ceased to occur altogether.

The University of London computer picked out individuals who had taken feverfew daily for different periods of time – one to six months, six to 12 months and so on. It then worked out the percentage who had benefited from taking it over these different periods of time. The results were that the effectiveness apparently improved with the duration of consumption. Some 90 per cent of those who had been eating feverfew leaves for more than two years felt that they were benefiting from it. One explanation for the apparent increase in effectiveness of feverfew when it is taken over a greater length of time is that those who felt it was not working had stopped taking the herb earlier. However, the data indicate that the beneficial effects of the plant do persist for as long as it is taken after an initial improvement in symptoms has been experienced.

Can feverfew be taken indefinitely?

Quite a number of migraine sufferers have now taken feverfew for more than five years, and a few that I have monitored have taken the plant for more than eight years. So, for how long is it advisable to continue treatment? There is no easy answer to this question.

Migraine is known to lessen in frequency and severity in many women as they pass through the menopause. Therefore, women whose periods stop while they are taking feverfew should make sure that they really need to carry on taking it. They should gradually tail off the number of leaves they take over two to four weeks so that, as the effects wear off, the body is able to adjust to the plant's chemicals no longer being present. If the underlying migraine process is still active, the attacks will return with their former intensity. Then, feverfew can be taken again and the migraine attacks should be suppressed as before.

Men and women who have taken feverfew for more than two years would be well advised to stop taking the leaves for at least one month each year to check whether it is still having a beneficial effect, as there is absolutely no point in taking any 'foreign' chemicals – whether in the form of synthetic drugs or plant drugs – if they are no longer necessary.

Also, the effects of feverfew on the unborn child are unknown and it would be a sensible precaution for any woman who becomes pregnant to stop taking the leaves straight away.

Additional beneficial effects of feverfew

Migraine sufferers taking feverfew attribute a number of pleasant effects to the plant, apart from the reduction in frequency and intensity of headaches. These include the prevention of nausea and vomiting, relief from symptoms of arthritis, a sense of well-being, more restful sleep and improved digestion. In all, 53 per cent of feverfew users claimed that taking the plants gave rise to pleasant side-effects and a minority of people seem to be very sensitive to them.

Whereas the unwanted side-effects of feverfew appeared early, the additional beneficial effects tended to coincide with the reduction or elimination of migraine. Thus, 17 per cent noted them during the first week, 33 per cent by the end of the first month and 67 per cent by the end of the second month. Of those who encountered adverse side-effects, 67 per cent did so within one week of starting to use feverfew. Furthermore, once the beneficial effects occurred, they continued for as long as the plant was taken. I have come across only two instances where this was not the case.

Relief of tension

In one of the double-blind trials, an elderly patient whose migraine had apparently spontaneously disappeared while he was taking feverfew leaves felt extremely nervous and on edge during the first two months on placebo capsules, even though his migraine headaches did not return. He recalled that he had felt like this before he had started taking feverfew. He was quite certain that feverfew had a calming action and that he was, therefore, being given the placebo. This calming property has been noted by many others.

4

Arthritis and other conditions

Feverfew has traditionally been used for easing inflammation, especially that associated with a fever. According to John Gerarde, writing in 1597, it is beneficial for 'all inflammation and hot swellings'. Since that time, and perhaps even before, it has been used to alleviate the symptoms of those conditions known collectively as the rheumatic diseases.

The rheumatic diseases – of which rheumatoid arthritis is the commonest form – affects joints, muscles and sinews, and usually give rise to considerable long-term discomfort, pain and stiffness which make the sufferer less mobile. As a few rheumatic diseases are potentially life-threatening, no one who has arthritic symptoms should consider self-medication until a firm diagnosis has been made by a doctor. Family doctors are used to treating rheumatic disorders, which, it has been calculated, account for about a fifth of their workload.

The symptoms of rheumatoid arthritis can abate spontaneously and someone who has suffered severe pain for some time, even for years, may experience a pain-free period for no apparent reason. These are the periods sufferers pray for when they do not find that the available medicines help them adequately.

Like migraine, rheumatoid arthritis cannot be rooted out and so treatment has to be directed at reducing the discomfort of the symptoms with drugs, physiotherapy, splints or surgery. Bed-rest is often of benefit. Also, there are two groups of drugs used to treat rheumatoid arthritis and these are called anti-inflammatory and anti-rheumatoid drugs.

There are many varieties of rheumatic conditions and so if you wish to know more, see *Copeman's Textbook of the Rheumatic Diseases*, edited by J. T. Scott.

More importantly, though, I would emphasize once again that before anyone considers self-medication of such a disease, they must be sure that it has been properly diagnosed by a medical practitioner to ensure that there are no more serious and undetected underlying conditions.

Self-help in arthritis

Probably in the region of 60 per cent of arthritis sufferers gain substantial relief from anti-inflammatory drugs, which decrease pain and stiffness. Not all respond to the same drugs, but someone who does not respond to one may well benefit from another. Unfortunately, the symptoms are suppressed only temporarily by these drugs – a few hours at best.

Aspirin is the oldest drug and still widely used. It does, however, have the disadvantage of having a fairly high incidence of side-effects even at the ordinary doses advocated by doctors. Also, some people become allergic to aspirin.

Some of the anti-inflammatory drugs – naproxen (Naprosyn) for example – combine greater effectiveness with a lower incidence of side-effects. They may also be taken less frequently than aspirin. Nevertheless, not all patients find full relief from their symptoms when they take these drugs and may be unable to take some medicines at all if they have additional conditions such as asthma, which is often made worse by anti-inflammatory drugs.

It is not surprising therefore that – as is the case with migraine – sufferers of arthritis have found many ways of helping themselves. Here are a few of the options.

Reducing weight

It is generally acknowledged that being overweight is not healthy. Osteoarthritis tends to affect the weight-bearing joints, those more prone to wear and tear or damaged from impact injuries as a result of sport, road accidents and so on. It follows that the greater the weight these joints have to support, the more likely it is that there will be degeneration of the joints, such as osteoarthritis. The inflamed joints of rheumatoid arthritis are similarly aggravated by excessive weight.

Unfortunately, putting on weight is only too easy if you have arthritis as painful joints tend to make you less mobile and less able to take adequate exercise.

Following a sensible diet with a view to losing excess weight – especially in cases where the hips or knees are affected – is probably the most important way those with arthritis can help ease their pain.

Bed rest

As pain and muscular spasm are largely determined by movement and weight-bearing, rest in bed is extremely helpful – especially for patients whose whole constitution is upset by fever or anaemia. However, patients must be encouraged to adopt a good posture and suitable non-weight-bearing exercises of the muscles must be undertaken to make up for the lack of movement.

Posture

Every effort should be made to correct faulty posture. This can be helped by wearing a collar or other spinal support.

Heat

The local application of a warm compress or hot water bottle to muscles before exercising reduces stiffness. Sufferers of osteoarthritis who have access to a heated swimming pool find that gentle movement of the affected joint under water relaxes the spasm of the surrounding muscles, reduces the pain and may increase the range of movement.

Stress

Many people who are tense and anxious complain of pains, particularly in the neck and back. Tension headaches may result from tension in the muscles at the back of the neck, which is a reaction to stress. Identifying the cause of the underlying anxiety may alleviate these symptoms.

Worry is known to precipitate recurrences of rheumatoid arthritis in sufferers whose symptoms have cleared. How this happens is not known, but stress can alter the body's chemistry, possibly making the joints and tissues more vulnerable to the causal factors. Certainly, it is easy to appreciate that the tenser the muscles are that are surrounding an inflamed joint, the more painful that joint will be.

Diet

The influence of diet on rheumatic disorders has been suspected, even claimed, to be of importance, but no good evidence has been proffered in favour of one or other specific diet.

Although diet is no longer considered to be a major causative factor in gout, some sufferers do claim that certain wines and foods, especially those containing chemicals that are converted in the body into uric acid (offal, fish, roe, meat extracts and so on), may precipitate attacks. These sufferers tend to exclude these substances from their diet.

Physical aids

People with arthritis spend a good deal of money on physical aids for the home, such as electric knives and can openers, pots with modified handles, liquidizers, bath seats, lavatory aids, long-handled combs and so on. It seems the expenditure is worth while as a survey carried out at the Centre for Rheumatic Diseases, Glasgow, revealed that these aids for the home provided far greater benefit than did prescribed medicines.

Natural remedies

As some arthritis sufferers do not receive much relief from prescribed medications, they try all manner of 'natural' products, such as an extract of the New Zealand green-lipped mussel, *Perna caniculus* (available from healthfood shops). It is claimed to relieve the symptoms of both rheumatoid and osteoarthritis, and is taken daily in the form of capsules, tablets or granules. However, when tested on animals, the results did not confirm these claims. The results of formal clinical trials on sufferers are awaited with interest. Fish oil has been shown to be of benefit in rheumatoid arthritis in a double-blind clinical trial.

The herbal remedies used by arthritis sufferers all require proper evaluation, but the following plants and alternative therapies have long been used in the treatment of arthritis.

- *White willow* The bark of the white willow contains salicin, a chemical like aspirin. Salicin was isolated from willow bark in around 1830 and it was used widely in the treatment of rheumatoid arthritis and to lower the body temperature in fever. Bark is gathered from young branches and air-dried. It is then shredded and usually taken as an infusion (tea).
- *Vernal grass* Baths and compresses prepared from sweet vernal grass (hay grass) are widely used for rheumatic conditions in continental Europe.
- *Black mustard* Compresses made from freshly ground black mustard seeds in hot water have been used for muscular pains, but extreme caution is required as the mustard mixture is highly irritant to the skin and can cause a serious inflammatory reaction. It should therefore be tested on a small area of the skin before using more widely.

- *Lavender* A liniment (rub) made from dried lavender flowers has been applied to the painful areas. Rosemary has been similarly used.
- *St John's wort* A liniment has also been made from the oil obtained from this plant.
- *Devil's claw (grapple plant)* An infusion made from the tuberous root of devil's claw has long been used in rheumatoid arthritis.
- *Juniper* It used to be advocated that an infusion made from the crushed berries of the common juniper be taken daily for one to two months during both spring and autumn by patients suffering from chronic rheumatism. Sometimes the juniper was replaced by shredded dandelion root or dried leaves of the stinging nettle.
- *Copper bracelets and acupuncture* The wearing of copper bracelets, which are cheap to buy, and acupuncture treatment, which is expensive, have been found to be of little benefit.

With the exception of the active ingredient known to be present in willow bark and the reports of the relief afforded by liniments, herbal treatments have undergone comparatively little evaluation. Indeed, from the information available, their efficacy appears to be poor.

Feverfew for painful joints

Following the publicity given to Mrs Jenkins' story that feverfew helped her symptoms of osteoarthritis, many users wrote confirming her experience. A retired farmer wrote of his wife and himself:

Our complaint is arthritis in the fingers, arms and shoulders. A friend of ours was taking feverfew for migraine. She was also crippled with arthritis, but, after a few months, she was partly cured of arthritis and migraine. So we gave it a try for our arthritis, which was rather bad with both of us having had it for about ten to 12 years. Since taking feverfew the pain got less until we had no pain. These last two years have been without any pain from arthritis. In our opinion it is due to taking feverfew. We have never had side-effects in any way.

A man suffering from cervical spondylosis wrote:

The effects of feverfew on my problem were swift. In a month, I was able to stop taking pain drugs and I have not taken any drug since and with leaving out drugs the feverfew effect was even more noticeable. Needless to say the doctors at Grimsby Hospital were astounded.

However, as we saw in the case of migraine, the story wasn't all one-sided. Some people found it did not help them at all and some reported side-effects, as before.

... my aim in trying to get it [feverfew] was to see if it would be beneficial in the treatment of osteoarthritis from which I suffer. Eventually I was able to obtain the plant locally – but, alas, I still have bad arthritis.

I should think that it might be very effective, but it proved something of a poison to me. I chewed two small leaves of it and was surprised to find my lips badly swollen quite soon afterwards. I thought that this might be due to some other cause so, a few days later I ate two more small leaves. My lips again became swollen and cracked to such an extent that a person calling on me thought that I had suffered a bad fall.

Personal testimonies such as these, though interesting, are of limited value in scientific terms. However, there are more definite indications that the leaves have some effect in rheumatoid arthritis. I have personally examined a few people who have the physical changes in the hands that are characteristic of rheumatoid arthritis. One of these claimed that she had been symptom-free for the five years she had been taking the leaves. Another found that her symptoms recurred only when she stopped taking the leaves.

In the migraine trial mentioned earlier, I switched patients (unbeknown to them) from capsules containing dried feverfew powder to those containing a placebo. When I did this, two female participants experienced severe aches and pains in their muscles and joints. In one, the pains remained localized in the muscles of the lower limbs and the knee joints, but the other experienced severe pains in several joints and muscle groups. The pains moved from day to day around her body and were accompanied by marked stiffness of the neck and shoulder joints, to such a degree that she was unable to turn her head. She also experienced brief but noticeable weakness in her ability to grip with her hands. In both women, the symptoms on withdrawal from feverfew persisted for almost two months before disappearing. About a tenth of 164 migraine-suffering feverfew users who stopped taking the herb experienced similar symptoms.

Experimental evidence supporting the anti-inflammatory effect of feverfew

Feverfew contains chemicals called the *sesquiterpene lactones*. Related sesquiterpene lactones from other plants have inhibited the development of arthritis in animals and some are more potent than the most active anti-inflammatory drug, indomethacin.

Several observations support the suggestion that feverfew might be beneficial in treating inflammatory conditions. The first, made in my laboratory at King's College, London, was that the sesquiterpene lactones in feverfew keep in check the biological actions of prostaglandins and histamine – substances released in large amounts during the inflammatory process. A second observation, made by scientists in Washington, was that extracts of feverfew actually suppressed the formation of prostaglandins. Finally, scientists in Nottingham found that feverfew inhibits certain functions of two blood cell types – platelets and leukocytes – involved in the process of inflammation.

Clinical trial of feverfew in rheumatoid arthritis

The question as to whether or not these laboratory studies had any relevance medically was investigated in 1988 when a double-blind comparison of the effects of feverfew and a placebo was carried out with rheumatoid arthritis sufferers in Nottingham. The participants were assessed over six weeks for joint stiffness, pain, strength of grip, joint size, mobility and a battery of blood tests. The groups of patients were matched for age and how long they had had arthritis. The average dose of standardized feverfew given was 76 mg, which is equivalent to taking two medium-sized leaves.

The trial showed that the participants taking feverfew experienced no easing of their symptoms during the six-week period. Although significant changes occurred in two of the factors examined (one in favour of, one against feverfew), this was said to be no more than was expected to happen by chance in a study examining a total of 21 variables.

For ethical reasons, the feverfew used in this study was added to the patients' conventional drug treatment, which presumably was helping to ease their symptoms to some degree. Nevertheless, it is highly likely that, at the dose used, feverfew was not also helping to relieve their arthritis. This suggests that the anti-inflammatory action noted in the laboratory tests on tissues and blood cells was of no relevance to how feverfew acted in the prevention of migraine as the dose of feverfew used in the rheumatoid arthritis trial was similar to that used in the study of migraine and, as we saw, at that level it acted to prevent migraine.

Using feverfew to treat other conditions

There seems to be no shortage of people who are prepared to try taking feverfew for a variety of conditions, some of whom have apparently improved markedly when they have followed the same treatment regimen used by migraine sufferers. Some are recorded here.

Ménière's syndrome

Ménière's syndrome is a condition the cause of which is unknown but which is characterized by recurrent bouts of severe dizziness or vertigo associated with ringing in the ears (tinnitus) and progressive irreversible deafness. Many sufferers also have a history of migraine. One such individual, a 79-year-old woman, completed the feverfew questionnaire and gave a detailed description of what happened when she took feverfew for her condition, which she had suffered for many years.

The giddiness was so severe that sometimes she was unable to stand. This was accompanied by severe nausea, vomiting, sweating and fainting. She obtained a complete and lasting remission when she took three small leaves of feverfew every day, and this remission has persisted for over two years. The sickness and vertigo have been more or less eradicated, too; before taking feverfew they used to last for hours. She now takes no other medicine for her Ménière's.

A result as striking as this must have been observed before. So what did Gerarde and Culpeper have to say? First Gerarde:

... it is very good for them that are giddie in the head, or which have the turning called Vertigo.

Now to Culpeper:

It is very effectual for all pains in the head coming of a cold cause ... As also for vertigo, that is a running or swimming in the head.

There is still no good conventional treatment for Ménière's syndrome, although antihistamines such as chlorpromazine (Largactil) and prochlorperazine (Stemetil) given three times every day sometimes reduce the number of attacks. As extracts of feverfew have also been found to have an antihistamine action, this might explain why the 79-year-old lady experienced such a beneficial effect.

Respiratory disorders

Feverfew has been used for centuries for the treatment of respiratory illnesses. Thus, according to Culpeper:

The decoction thereof made, with some sugar, or honey put thereto, is used by many with good success to help the cough and stuffing of the chest, by colds, ... The powder of the herb taken in wine, with some Oxymel, purges both choler and phlegm, and is available for those that are short winded ...

Dodoens, writing in 1578, said:

Feverfew dried and made into pouder, and two drammes of it taken with hony, or other thing, purgeth by siege Melancholy and fleume: where for it is very good ... for them that are purse or troubled with shortnes of winde, ...

That feverfew has traditionally been used to treat colds is indicated by the following extract from a letter to the British Migraine Association:

My great grandmother was a herb woman and knowledge of this plant has been passed down by word of mouth. But our granny grew it in a London garden, and she picked the plant, leaves and flowers, and poured boiling water over it. When cold we drank it in a small wine glass. This was when we had bad colds and headaches with stomach upsets.

The 'headaches with stomach upsets' is most probably a reference to the folk use of feverfew in the treatment of migraine.

Feverfew has also been used in the treatment of asthma:

I have suffered from asthma for over 20 years, and believing there is a link between migraine, asthma and eczema, I started taking feverfew . . .

After taking feverfew since 1978 (four years), the result is remarkable. I have been able to reduce the amount of cortisone I have been taking for many years and feel altogether better. I used to be a wheezing invalid, but no longer, thanks to feverfew.

Insect bites

Mrs Lesley Hirst, whose recipe for feverfew pills can be found on pages 51–2 made some interesting observations. Before she took feverfew, she used to react violently to insect bites, especially mosquito bites, which caused marked, inflamed swelling. Since she started taking feverfew, she never seems to react to insect bites and wonders whether she is now no longer being bitten.

One possible explanation is that Mrs Hirst is being bitten just as often but that the inflammatory reaction to the insect bites is being suppressed by the chemicals in the feverfew that have been absorbed into the body. The antihistamine action of the plant may be particularly important in this respect.

It may also possess insecticidal activity, as members of the *Chrysanthemum* and *Tanacetum* plant families are well known to contain chemicals protective against insect attack. Tansy, in particular, is still kept in the dried form to repel insects.

Other conditions

Several other experimenters have been prepared to try feverfew for more serious conditions. I shall mention two of them only as a means of discouraging other would-be users who have these illnesses from doing the same.

A lady from Hampshire wrote to me and told how she took feverfew for brucellosis, or undulant fever – a bacterial infection transmitted from cattle to humans via unpasteurized milk. She took feverfew for some time then, fortunately in her case, 'saw an article in *Woman's Weekly* which said it was toxic to the liver' and so stopped taking it.

Brucellosis, once diagnosed, should be treated only with the appropriate antibiotics, otherwise the symptoms of sweating, weakness, headache, loss of appetite, pain in the limbs, joints and back, cough and sore throat may recur intermittently for many months.

A man, also from Hampshire, took feverfew for 12 months to treat a serious attack of glaucoma and experienced no improvement.

Glaucoma is a condition of the eye characterized by an increase in the pressure of the fluid within the eyeball. The pressure can be so high that the retina at the back of the eye can be damaged and blindness can result. As effective conventional treatments are available, no one diagnosed as having glaucoma should take feverfew or any other drug or herbal preparation to treat it without medical supervision.

I have had reports from other people who have used feverfew for multiple sclerosis and other life-threatening conditions. It is understandable that individuals with progressively deteriorating conditions for which there is no known cure should grasp at any straw, but taking feverfew for potentially fatal disorders should always be done with a doctor's knowledge and agreement.

5

The immigrant

Feverfew is not indigenous to Britain. It was probably originally brought to this country for medicinal purposes by the Romans, although some authorities believe that it came later, in Anglo-Saxon times. It gradually became a plant that was grown in most gardens and also escaped to the hedgerows and dry stone walls to which it is so well suited. It was similarly introduced into North America as a medicinal plants by the early colonists.

Feverfew's Latin name is *Tanacetum parthenium* (L) Schultz Bip., formerly *Chrysanthemum parthenium*, and, according to the writer Plutarch, it acquired the name parthenium because it was used to save the life of a person who fell off the Parthenon during its construction in the fifth century BC. Another view is that the name derives from *parthenios*, which is Greek for 'virgin', reflecting the herb's use in the treatment of gynaecological problems. Feverfew is almost certainly the plant called 'Parthenion' by Dioscorides in his herbal, compiled in the first century AD. Its common English name, feverfew, feverfue or federfoy, was possibly inspired by the feather-like leaves, although it is more likely to be derived from its Saxon name feferfuge or feferfugia (Latin *febrifugia*), meaning 'that which dispels a fever'. Certainly, it was used for this purpose.

Alternative medieval Latin names include *Amaracus*, *Matricaria* and *Amarella*. The English also knew it as midsummer daisy, featherfew, whitewurte and St Peter's wurt, the French as espargoutte or matricaire, and the Germans as Mutterkraut.

The confusion over names

Although feverfew is an easy plant to identify, some people find its various botanical names confusing. In fact, only one name is correct botanically for any plant at any one time, but plant names are changed from time to time and feverfew was recently reclassified, moving from the *Chrysanthemum* to the *Tanacetum* (tansy) genus. Naturally, once a name has come to be widely accepted and used, it takes a long time to establish the new name and this has been true of feverfew. There is no longer any justification for ascribing it to the Chamomile genus, *Matricaria*, or to the genus *Pyrethrum*.

Varieties of plant species are correctly written with 'var.' appearing between the species name and variety name. Thus, the golden variety of feverfew is *Tanacetum parthenium* var. 'aureum', but often the 'var.' is omitted.

Feverfew, or *Tanacetum parthenium* (L) Schultz Bip.

How to identify feverfew plants

Common feverfew is very different from other plants bearing the name feverfew, such as sea-feverfew, corn feverfew, and sweet feverfew. It grows in most parts of the British Isles and is often found growing wild in old gardens and on waste land, where it thrives almost as well as when it is cultivated. It will, in fact, grow almost anywhere and certainly seems to enjoy rooting between the stones of walls such as those found in Britain in Devon, North Wales and Yorkshire. It grows throughout Europe, North America, North Africa, China, Japan and Australasia. It is not averse to shade, but tends to grow most prolifically in sunny spots.

Many people all over the world are now growing feverfew, not only to provide them with sufficient leaves throughout the year, but

46

also as an ornamental plant for the herbaceous border. It is a perennial, growing to a height of 14 to 45 cm (5½ to 17¾ inches) with yellow-green leaves that are deeply cut to form five or more leaflets. The leaves have an extremely strong and characteristic aromatic odour when crushed. They also taste bitter. The attractive daisy-like flowers, which can measure almost 2 cm (¾ in) across in the right growing conditions, form loose, flat-topped clusters of 5 to 30 flowers. The flowers have flat yellow centres with short and broad, white petals. The flowers give way to small flattened, ribbed seeds.

The feverfew flowers from late June to October, but the long, woody, flower-bearing stems provide fewer of the leaves that are suitable for medicinal use. For this reason, many users nip out the flower buds of three-quarters of their plants, allowing only a few to go on to provide seed for propagation purposes.

Ornamental feverfews

Other kinds of feverfew plants can be grown for ornamental purposes. The golden varieties look especially lovely at the front of a border. These plants are smaller than the common feverfew and have beautiful golden leaves which hug the ground and little button flowers that bloom from July to October. They do well in a sunny position and, like the common variety, remain in leaf throughout winter. The variety 'Golden Ball' grows to a height of about 20 cm (7¾ inches); 'Golden Moss' is shorter, the double, white, cultivated varieties 'Sissinghurst White', 'Ball's Double White' and 'White Bonnet' grow to the same height as common feverfew. They make superb edging plants.

The leaves of the cultivated varieties contain chemicals similar to those of common feverfew and are probably similarly effective when used medicinally, although this has to be verified. Until this is done, you should only use common feverfew (*Tanacetum parthenium*). The cultivated varieties are often the ones to be found on sale at garden centres and nurseries.

Where to obtain feverfew plants

Many thousands of people world-wide now grow feverfew for medicinal or ornamental purposes and are usually only too willing to pass on seedlings. If you don't know anyone who grows feverfew, however, ask at your local garden centre or herb nursery. Those stocking common feverfew and the varieties mentioned above are listed in the *RHS Plant Finder* edited by Tony Lord. This information is also available on CD-ROM, entitled *The Plant Finder Library*.

How to grow and propagate feverfew

Choose a sunny bed containing well-drained soil and dig in compost or rotted grass cuttings. There is no need to worry about removing any stones. Seedlings can be planted out at any time if they are being transferred from an outside bed. They should be planted about 0.6 metre (2 feet) apart, unless they are being grown to provide cuttings, when they can be planted 0.3 metre (1 foot) apart, as alternate plants will be removed eventually. To ensure a good supply of leaves, each person taking feverfew needs at least three, but preferably four or five plants.

Feverfew seeds usually germinate well, provided they are less than one year old. Their germination rate is considerably reduced if they are allowed to become too dry for long periods. Sow the seeds in 1.25-cm (½-inch) deep furrows in trays containing garden soil or a multipurpose compost and when the seedlings are 2.5 cm (1 inch) high, pot them out into 5-cm (2-inch) diameter pots. You will find then that the roots are very well formed and even on the smaller seedlings they can be 5 to 7.5 cm (3 inches) in length. The plants can either be 'potted on' into 12.5 to 15-cm (5 to 6-inch) pots and kept in a cold frame or planted out into beds when the spread of stems and leaves is 5 to 7.5 cm (2 to 3 inches). They are extremely hardy.

Feverfew will also grow indoors and it is especially useful to do this in winter to keep a steady supply of leaves. When grown inside, the plants require plenty of light, warmth and daily watering to ensure a lush growth of leaves.

Feverfew can be propagated from cuttings taken from a plant of any age, but it does particularly well if these are taken from one-year-old plants after they have flowered, when the woody stems have died back. Roots grow down from the junction between a new shoot and the old stem, but the most reliable form of propagation is by root cuttings.

To take root cuttings, first lift the plant and shake off the soil, then, using a sharp blade, slit the main stem along its mid-line upwards through the leaves, and downwards through the main root. These two halves of the plant can then be planted out in beds or pots.

Feverfew plants can also be propagated from leaves. Simply dip the stems of sprigs of new growth in hormone rooting powder and plant in wet soil in little pots. They should develop roots 2.5 to 5 cm (1 to 2 inches) in length within 14 days. Note, however that with this method the failure rate is high unless you are expert at it.

Pests and other insects and disease

In a wet year, feverfew is susceptible to mildew and young plants may well be subject to damping off (a disease in which the seedlings collapse and die as their roots darken and rot off). Blackfly can be troublesome on new shoots in late spring, but they can be washed off with a hose.

As with chrysanthemums, when the plants are in flower, watch out for earwigs in wet weather.

Ladybirds and white spiders seem to be particularly attracted to the plant, especially when the seedheads are ripening.

If in doubt

The physical appearance of feverfew is so distinct from the related chrysanthemums, tansies and chamomiles that correctly identifying it should not be a problem. I have encountered only one person among 300 surveyed who was not actually eating feverfew leaves, though she thought she was. Of 20 other people who were not absolutely certain as to what they were taking, all of them turned out to be eating feverfew leaves. Even suppliers can make mistakes. About 12 years ago, herbal suppliers in Britain, endeavouring to obtain feverfew samples, received incorrectly both German chamomile and tansy from Eastern Europe (quoted by Dr M. I. Berry, *The Pharmaceutical Journal*, 19 May, 1984). If, therefore, you are in doubt as to the identity of a plant, check first with your local nurseryman, horticultural society or the botany department of the nearest university. Otherwise, consult one of the floras in the reference section of your local public library, such as the *Flora Europeae*, (Volume 4, Cambridge University Press, 1976). However, remember, plants can be harmful so be sure before you try and, if in doubt, don't! In any case, anyone wishing to try feverfew should discuss this first with their doctor.

Feverfew on holiday and in winter

When migraine sufferers stop taking feverfew after several months of daily use, their attacks quickly return. This can be so disabling that some people restrict their movements to within a day's journey from their source of supply. These people, although relatively few in number, never take holidays and when they are suddenly and unexpectedly faced with the prospect of journeying to foreign parts, become stricken with panic and refuse to go. Unfortunately they have not heard of the alternative means of taking feverfew (see pages 51 to 54).

Winter, too, brings its problems as plant growth may be severely retarded at this time and not everybody is able to pot up the plants and take them indoors. A 71-year-old retired Major from south-west London wrote:

> In recent springs and summers I have had great relief from eating a morning sandwich of a tablespoonful of feverfew leaves in bread but face a long winter without abatement of migraine almost three or four times each week because the plant does not show leaf again until January/February (if then). I have continuously asked all over the country why no tablet or 'infusion' is available from 'health' shops – the usual reaction is: 'never heard of it!' You will be doing many thousands of sufferers a great service if you can persuade the Ministry or in some way promote the provision of feverfew in some other form than the leaves taken fresh from the plant, so that it can be taken in liquid or tablet form during the 'fall' and winter. I can assure you that it works – without it I am entirely dependent on diet and Migril which I have taken for 30 years.

In fact, advertisements for dried feverfew tablets capsules or powder frequently appear in health magazines and they are available from shops in the UK. No commercially available tablets and capsules have been properly assessed for safety and efficacy and so those containing high doses of feverfew (over 125 mg) or for which the dose is not specified are better avoided. Tablets containing 25 mg of dried feverfew permit some adjustment of dose to be made without the danger of taking too much.

There is no convincing evidence that homoeopathic feverfew preparations are effective in relieving migraine either. Indeed, the use of a dilution of feverfew runs counter to basic homoeopathic principles. Of some 20 patients I have encountered using the 6X homoeopathic potency feverfew tablets, only one of them thought they might be of benefit.

Capsules and tablets mask the bitter taste of the plant and are easy to take on holiday. They also serve as an ideal stop-gap when the leaves have been covered with frost or snow during winter. However, despite being convenient, they are by no means the only alternative way of taking feverfew.

Granules of 'chrysanthemum' powder mixed with cane sugar and imported from China are marketed widely in health food shops as feverfew. I know of many who have tried a sachet or teaspoonful each day as an infusion and have found it of benefit, although others have experienced palpitations and a rapid pulse rate. As there is some doubt as to whether the contents really are *Tanacetum parthenium*, it is probably wiser not to take this mixture.

Air-dried leaves and powdered feverfew leaves can be obtained from qualified herbalists and some herb suppliers. If you pack these leaves separately between layers of clingfilm or foil, you can measure your daily dose accurately. If the dried leaves are crushed, it is difficult to measure out daily doses, but, according to Mrs Jenkins, a heaped ordinary salt spoon is the equivalent of a large fresh leaf.

Many users have solved the supply problems in other ways. Some pick long, leaf-bearing stalks and put them into bottles that have rubber seals – the sort used to transport single orchids through the post. This works quite well, but if the leaves are kept under water, they will rot and give off a putrid odour.

Mrs Lesley Hirst of Kent has discovered an ingeniously simple way to prepare what she calls dried feverfew 'tablets' and sends out the following instructions to people who ask her for feverfew plants.

How to make dried feverfew tablets

Dry 100 feverfew leaves on a sheet of kitchen roll in your airing cupboard. When completely dry, crush the leaves as small as possible (an electric liquidizer is ideal). Mix the crushed leaves with 75 g (3 oz) icing sugar and approximately $1\frac{1}{2}$ teaspoons of cold water to form a very stiff dough that can easily be handled. Then pick off small pieces of the mixture and roll them into pea-sized balls. Dredge a baking tray with icing sugar and place the wet 'tablets' on this. Place in an airing cupboard for about 24 hours to dry the tablets thoroughly and then store in an airtight container. You should be able to make 100 tablets from this recipe, therefore take two tablets daily in place of the fresh leaves.

Although Mrs Hirst's recipe will produce pills containing varying amounts of feverfew, they probably do not vary in weight much more than raw leaves do from day to day. Furthermore, she has taken the important step of producing a 'standard leaf' unit and in this way protects herself from accidentally taking too much, which can easily occur when the dried powder is used. An early sign of overdose is abdominal pain and purging, which may last for a couple of days. One lady in her forties who had never taken feverfew before took a heaped teaspoonful of finely powdered feverfew just to see what it would taste like. She found the taste quite acceptable – 'herby' – but not the colicky diarrhoea that followed.

Drying feverfew

Users find that dried feverfew seems to work just as well as the raw leaves. When patients at the City of London Migraine Clinic in England changed from taking raw leaves to capsules containing the equivalent in powder to their daily dose of leaves for the purposes of the trial, they noticed no difference between the two (see Chapter 3).

A lady from the North of England who suffered from disabling migraine with aura visited me at the clinic in May 1981. She had been taking feverfew since 1978 and had had no more attacks from that time onwards. She was greatly worried about a forthcoming visit to Australia and New Zealand that was to take her away from England for ten months. I suggested that she might dry sufficient feverfew during the next three months to cover the duration of her trip. On her return she gave me the following progress report:

Further to my visit to you on May 26th 1981, I have to report the following progress with the use of *dried* feverfew during my absence from England between August 11th 1981 and June 19th 1982 . . .

On Dec. 2nd 1981 I experienced the first stage of a migraine – visual disturbance – but it went no further.

On May 10th 1981 I had the visual disturbance followed by another lot on May 15th. Neither went beyond the first stage.

We returned to England on June 19th when I resumed taking fresh feverfew but I had another bout of visual disturbance on July 4th and again on August 2nd. Once more there was no development beyond the first stage.

Since then I have been free of any further attacks – and hope to continue so!

Whilst in New Zealand I gave some dried feverfew to a friend who has suffered with migraine for many years. The effect was instantaneous, unlike the time lapse of three months I experienced, and she has been clear of any attacks since first taking feverfew in December 1981.

Although many users still eat raw leaves, an increasing number are taking to the dried form or tablets.

A little folklore appears to be building up around the drying procedure – that the leaves should be picked in the morning on a sunny day when the dew has dried and shouldn't be washed and other such rules. Take my advice instead! Pick them at any time of day, wet or dry, and wash them thoroughly under cold water. Remove as much of the excess water as possible in a salad spinner or shake vigorously in a colander and then dry on blotting paper or kitchen role in an airing cupboard or a dry, well-ventilated room. To ensure that the leaves dry evenly, turn them at intervals. It is important to check that the leaves have dried completely as otherwise they will attract mildew and be unusable. As a guide, completely dry leaves weigh approximately one sixth of their wet weight.

Fresh feverfew leaves keep well in the freezer until required, when they can be thawed and used immediately. Freezing helps to break up the cells and release the active contents. The frozen leaves may also be dried at a later date in the same way as fresh ones and can be powdered before or after the drying process.

Store the dried leaves in an air-tight container, such as a glass preserving jar. Ensure the complete dryness of the storage jar by putting a muslin bag containing a suitable drying agent, such as silica gel, into the jar with the leaves.

Masking the taste

Most users cannot stand the extremely bitter taste of the leaves – reminiscent of camphor or quinine – and do not persevere with them for this reason. Most of those who do persist have found ways of masking the taste and here are some ideas that you might like to try.

A popular method – one advocated by Mrs Ann Jenkins – is to eat the leaves in a bread and butter sandwich to which some honey or sugar has been added. Indeed, this echoes traditional herbalists' advice as honey was recommended in the old herbals for disguising the taste of the leaves.

Others chop up the leaves and sprinkle them over their meal as a garnish, rather like you would chopped parsley.

Mrs Hirst, whose recipe for dried feverfew tablets appears on page 51, sent the following advice.

If, like me, you find the leaves utterly disgusting to eat, try the following method.

Take a jelly cube and, using a sharp knife, cut a hole in the centre. Turn the cube on its side so that you can see how deep the hole is, then cut across the cube just below the hole. Turn the cube upright again and trim off the corners to a 'swallowable' size. Roll up two feverfew leaves and stuff them into the hole. The cube is then quite palatable to swallow with a drink.

An arthritis sufferer who finds her daily doses of feverfew help her disguises the taste by chewing two leaves with a date. Another lady who has rheumatoid arthritis takes her dose with crispbread and cottage cheese. Others mix it with chopped parsley or take it with salad.

How much and how should it be taken?

Most feverfew users eat two or three raw leaves every day as a preventive for either migraine or arthritis.

Some people use feverfew in much larger doses to ward off a

THE IMMIGRANT

migraine attack as soon as they get the first warning signs. Taking a heaped tablespoonful is not unusual and it seems to work. I have heard of an interesting variation on this from a woman who wrote to me about a migraine attack which occurred as she was buying vegetables from a local allotment holder.

It was a very sunny day and I could have cried with the pain, it was so bad . . .
The allotment holder told me he had just the thing to give me relief. He then gave me the leaves of the plant and told me to chew them for a little while, swallowing the juices but not the leaves.
I was a little wary at first as the taste was very bitter. But the relief was unbelievable.

Feverfew was used traditionally to treat acute attacks of inflammatory disorders. It was given in a single high dose of 2 drams of powder taken with honey, which is equivalent to 3.5 g ($\frac{1}{8}$ oz). This is about the weight of 140 dried small leaves (those measuring 3.75 by 3.25 cm/1$\frac{1}{2}$ by 1$\frac{1}{4}$ inches). This single dose, recommended by the writers of the herbals for the treatment of such acute attacks, is equivalent to more than the average amount consumed over two months when it is used as a preventive. It is the herb's use as a preventive that is the innovation, largely pioneered by Mrs Ann Jenkins.

Even larger amounts – such as 25 g (1 oz) of leaves and flowers – were used for the purpose of making an infusion or tea, and still are by some people.

6

Is feverfew safe?

The serious birth defects that resulted when pregnant women took the sedative drug thalidomide more than 30 years ago still haunt the drug industry. That it had this effect first came to light in West Germany in 1961, five years after the introduction of the drug. Eventually the real extent of the tragedy was counted in terms of tens of thousands of malformed babies in some 15 countries.

Thalidomide had been prescribed widely, and even sold over the counter without prescription, for a relatively trivial condition and a horrified public rightly demanded to know how this had come about. Why was the drug not tested on pregnant animals before marketing? Why hadn't these appalling defects come to light during the early stages of testing in man? Who was to blame? Why had the US Food and Drug Administration (FDA) not approved the marketing of thalidomide when so many other countries had?

In 1962, largely as a result of questions such as these, a joint subcommittee of the English and Scottish Standing Medical Advisory Committees recommended the establishment of an expert committee to review the evidence available for the reasonable safety of new drugs used for their intended purpose. The Committee on Safety of Drugs came into being in 1963 under the chairmanship of Sir Derrick Dunlop, and drug companies voluntarily submitted their evidence to the Dunlop Committee, as it came to be known. Eventually the Committee was given statutory backing and the Medicines Act received the Royal Assent in October 1968.

The Act controls many aspects of the development, testing, manufacture, distribution, marketing and labelling of medicines for human and veterinary use. Importantly, the Act embraces the principles that medicines must be manufactured to an appropriate quality and must be efficacious and safe for their intended use.

UK health ministers are given the legal authority to issue certificates and licences to permit the drug industry to undertake clinical trials and manufacture and sell medicines. Health ministers are politicians responsible for ensuring that decisions are made on the quality, safety and efficacy of medicines, but are themselves rarely qualified to make such decisions. Accordingly, the Govern-

56

ment's Medicines Control Agency (MCA) undertakes this task on behalf of ministers.

The MCA is an executive agency that is empowered to make decisions relating to the use of medicines and to issue licences and certificates to the drug industry. To assist the MCA (but, in a legal sense, the health ministers), expert advice on the issuing of licences for new drugs and on matters of safety is provided by an independent body of medical, pharmaceutical and scientific experts known as the Committee on Safety of Medicines (CSM). In effect, it continues the work of the former Committee on Safety of Drugs.

It is recognized that the law can never keep up with the pace of development and advances in science in the drug industry. Accordingly, the MCA and the CSM issue guidelines to the drug industry on the data required to demonstrate quality, safety and efficacy. These guidelines are constantly updated to ensure that appropriate studies are undertaken and that inappropriate studies are avoided. New guidelines are introduced periodically to take account of new techniques for testing medicines and some old guidelines are dropped as a result.

Following the thalidomide tragedy, many governments established their own laws for controlling medicines. In Europe, this led to a plethora of executive and advisory bodies, each with its own procedures and guidelines. This made developing single medicines that could be sold in the whole of Europe extremely complicated. Sometimes inappropriate repetition of clinical or animal tests occurred in order to meet specific local requirements.

The paradox of more and more tests on animals being required while the public was demanding tighter control of animal experimentation and less of it, was recognized and was also seen as a barrier to the development of the Single European Market, a cornerstone of the European Union. Therefore, in the last ten years, the European Union has worked diligently to harmonize its national laws and guidelines on medicines. Thus, guidelines that are applicable to all member states of the European Union are now issued by a central European regulatory advisory group – the Committee for Proprietary Medicinal Products, which comprises medical, pharmaceutical and scientific experts from each member state.

The pressure of regulatory harmonization throughout the world has been gaining pace. The major countries of Europe, the USA and

Japan are now working to harmonize medicines guidelines under the auspices of the International Conference on Harmonization. This ambitious project will eventually lead to world-wide guidelines on the development and testing of new medicines and, hopefully, reduce the unnecessary repetition of tests on animals and the excessive exposure of human beings to new drugs during clinical trials, protecting the welfare of both animals and humans.

Tests on animals

The pharmacologist's job is to predict efficacy and safety on the basis of the finds of tests on animals. A major drug company may produce thousands of new compounds each year and pharmacologists have about a hundred ways of testing these on each of about ten species. It would be physically, if not economically, impossible to use all the tests available, so pharmacologists select a few of them that, based on past experience, are most likely to yield useful information. These form the screening programme and must show up active compounds and reject inactive or harmful ones as quickly as possible.

The first test is commonly carried out using laboratory mice. Groups of mice are given different doses of a prospective new drug and carefully observed to detect any slight departures from the normal that might suggest that the compound has, for example, sedative, antidepressant, muscle relaxant, painkilling or antihypertensive properties. The results are compared with those obtained using standard drugs that have known, well-established pharmacological effects.

The drug then undergoes more specialized evaluation of the effects observed in the tests on mice. Complicated tests are carried out on higher mammals and on isolated tissues and, at this stage, it is decided whether or not the effects discovered warrant testing for safety (toxicity).

Toxicity tests – tests of the potential damage the drugs or chemicals could cause – are of two main kinds:

- *acute tests* last for only a short time
- *chronic tests* require the repeated dosing of animals over weeks, months or years.

The drugs are administered in the same way that they are intended to be taken by human beings.

Increasing dose tolerance tests

These are acute toxicity tests, the object of which is to quantify if or how toxic the drug is. They are useful for determining doses of drugs for subsequent repeat-dose studies in animals and for identifying those organs particularly sensitive to the damaging effects of the drug.

Chronic toxicity tests

These are long-term toxicity tests of drugs that are intended to be given by mouth for more than 30 days and usually last for 26 weeks in the United Kingdom and 12 weeks, followed by a second study of a year, in the USA.

Four groups of each of two species are used. One group is given the maximum tolerated dose, which is chosen to induce effects on the most sensitive organs and tissues during the period of the study, but is at a level that is low enough not to kill most of the animals. The second group is given two or three times the maximum therapeutic dose intended for humans. The third group receives a dose in between these two and the fourth group is given no drug at all so that it can serve as a control for the test groups. In every other respect, the control and test animals are treated identically and observed carefully throughout the test period. After 26 weeks (in the UK), the organs of all the animals are examined to see if any dose-related toxic changes have occurred.

Reproductive toxicology tests

A drug's potential for inducing fetal abnormalities is looked for in the teratology studies, which have been required by the CSM since the experience with thalidomide.

The drug is given throughout the pregnancies of animals, commencing immediately after they have been mated. Again, four groups are used, a control group being observed once more to assess how frequently malformations would occur naturally. The resulting litters are examined for any deformities or abnormalities.

Another statutory test is that of fertility and general reproduction in which both males and females are given doses of the drug prior to mating. These tests are designed to discover whether or not a drug suppresses fertility or induces changes in the development of the animals' sperm. Many of the animals are allowed to deliver their litters and some offspring are allowed to mature, then themselves mated so that a second generation can be studied to see if the drug produces changes in fertility in the second generation.

The first clinical tests in humans may be initiated before the results of the reproductive toxicology tests are known. However, women of child-bearing age are specifically excluded from these studies until the results of the reproductive toxicology tests show that is safe for them to participate.

Mutagenicity (ability to alter chromosomes) test

This test shows whether or not a drug is able to induce changes in the structures called *chromosomes*, through which the genetic code is transmitted from parents to offspring or – in the case of multiplying bodily cells – from parent to daughter cells. Positive results sometimes indicate that the drug might cause cancer and negative results that this is less likely.

Carcinogenicity (ability to induce cancer) tests

These test whether or not drugs can induce cancer. They are mandatory if people are likely to take the new drug for more than a year. In any species, tumours take a long time to develop and may arise spontaneously. For these reasons, large groups of animals have to be used for these tests (50 of each sex per group) and a large control group is included (100 of each sex).

Animals that have just been weaned are dosed daily for the rest of their lives, which is 18 months for mice, two years for rats, eight years for dogs and so on. The top dose given is the highest that will still permit growth, while the other doses are as for six month-long chronic toxicity tests.

Two species have to be used that handle the drug in a manner similar to man, where this is known. Furthermore, they must be sensitive to chemicals known to induce cancer in humans. Regulatory guidelines stipulate what examinations using microscopes must be made at the end of such studies and the drug companies have to retain specimens for many years after the tests have been completed.

The first clinical tests on humans can be initiated before the results of the carcinogenicity studies are known, but, first, all the data from the animal studies have to be assembled along with data on the purity and stability of any one drug chemical and how it is formulated into tablets or capsules. This information is sent to the Medicines Control Agency with a request to undertake clinical trials.

Tests on human volunteers

The clinical investigation of a new drug is generally subdivided into the following four phases.

Phase 1

This phase is designed to confirm that the drug is as safe for man as it proved to be in the tests on animals.

In this phase, the drug is given to man for the first time. As the first dose given is usually less than that considered likely to benefit a patient with a disease, it is normally given to a healthy volunteer. Not only are the researchers interested in whether or not the drug induces the anticipated beneficial change to any degree, such as a lowering of blood pressure or slowing of the heart beat, but, more importantly, in whether or not there are any adverse effects on the body. This latter aspect is determined by examining blood and urine samples to see if there are any abnormalities. These tests are likely to pick up early cellular and chemical signs of liver, kidney and bone marrow damage before any symptoms become apparent. If the tests are negative, the next volunteer receives twice the initial dose and the whole procedure is repeated.

When, eventually, the doses given are within the range envisaged for treatment, a volunteer may be given more than one dose on successive days. Phase 1 ends with the repeated dosage of people who have the medical problem the drug is intended to treat, using a dose and regimen that has been calculated as a result of the studies carried out on the healthy volunteers. All the data regarding a drug's safety gathered from the blood tests are analysed before proceeding further. The number of people (both healthy volunteers and sufferers) taking part in phase 1 will usually be in the range of 20 to 50 who receive the new drug.

Phase 2

This is when substantial clinical trials are carried out involving people who have the particular ailment or disease concerned. These are designed to demonstrate how effective the drugs are and whether or not they are as safe as the results of phase 1 indicated. In this phase the dose that has the most beneficial effects is established with a fair degree of certainty, as is the dose that produces toxic effects.

Phase 2 seldom has more than 300 people taking the new treatment. These people are closely monitored and full blood tests are made from time to time. The trials are also usually controlled – that is, the new drug is compared with either an established treatment or a placebo (see page 29). The two clinical trials testing the effectiveness of feverfew for treating migraine discussed in chapter 3 would be classed as phase 2 studies.

Phase 3

More people receive the drug in controlled and uncontrolled trials in phase 3. Further evidence of the treatment's safety, the body's tolerance of it and a more precise definition of side-effects is obtained. Up to 3,000 people may have received the drug by the end of this phase. In the UK, the CSM usually requires that at least 100 patients have taken the drug continuously for more than a year if the treatment is to be taken daily for a condition such as high blood pressure or migraine prevention, when it will be used continuously for several years.

At the end of phase 3, all the clinical results are submitted to the Medicines Control Agency in the UK with an application for a product licence. Once this is granted, the drug can be marketed.

Phase 4

These trials take place after marketing has commenced. They include investigation into any rarer adverse reactions, especially those which may occur only when the person concerned has been taking the drug for a long time. Examples of such delayed adverse effects are the eye damage caused by the drug Eraldin or thrombosis experienced by women taking the higher dose oestrogen Pill. Often, the new drug is also tested to see if it has specific advantages over well-established competitive products.

Herbal medicines

The Medicines Act of 1968 initially exempted herbal remedies from licensing requirements and did not restrict their availability. Subsequently, the legislation passed in 1977 restricted the sale and supply of certain potent plant products to pharmacies, while still permitting qualified herbalists to prescribe some of them within certain dose ranges. In the mid 1980s, the Committee on Review of Medicines (CRM) examined licensed herbal remedies, requiring documentation of their quality, safety and efficacy. The CRM was prepared to accept published evidence of efficacy even when this was anecdotal rather than proven by clinical trial.

If a herbal remedy is sold without a claim for efficacy in a disease, then it does not require a product licence. Instead of being classed as a medicine, it is classed as a food supplement. Retailers sometimes get round the law by displaying pamphlets on benefits near the remedy in question.

The quality control of commercially available unlicensed herbal remedies varies markedly from product to product. In 1986, scientists from Nottingham examined selected feverfew products by testing their effects on blood cells and compared the results with those obtained using fresh leaves. They found that herbal feverfew products always contained smaller amounts of the herb than would be anticipated from the dose stated on the container, probably because of the variable content of stalk and leaf. They echoed our conclusions from the first study concerning feverfew and migraine, that it would be desirable for commercial preparations of feverfew to be standardized.

The safety of feverfew – the results of animal studies

To my knowledge, no formal chronic toxicity tests have yet been carried out for feverfew because its use as a preventive treatment for migraine was initiated by sufferers who used it and not by the drug industry. Therefore, because people tested feverfew on themselves and only now are experiments being performed on animals, the path of its development as a treatment has been exactly opposite to that which new medicines usually follow.

Rats trained to eat their normal diet in powdered form have been given measured amounts of feverfew powder mixed into their food. They readily ate more than 100 times the average human daily dose every day. Furthermore, they did so for five successive weeks without any loss of appetite or difference in weight gain when compared with control animals that were given only their normal powdered diet. Similarly, guinea-pigs ate about 150 times the average human dose every day and, after seven weeks, were identical in every respect to the control animals – their coats looked as sleek and their weight gain was the same.

Feverfew, therefore, appears to satisfy the preferred requirement of all new drugs, which is that the dose required to produce a therapeutic effect in man is less than 100th and, preferably, less than 150th of the dose that will cause serious toxic effects. Although what constitutes a toxic dose of feverfew has not yet been determined in animals, judging by the observations detailed above, it is likely to be extremely high. However, the tests that have been carried out were of short duration compared with those that would satisfy a regulatory authority. Interestingly, extensive toxicity tests have been carried out on a feverfew product approved by the authorities in Canada and the results showed that 'an extremely benign profile has been found', but as I have not seen the data it is not possible to comment further.

As far as I can tell from the long-term human users I have examined and whose blood has been tested, no serious side-effects have yet emerged. I would emphasize the 'yet', however, because three to five years is not long in the life of a drug. Remember, the effects of thalidomide were not identified until five years after it started to be marketed and used. Often, the rarer adverse effects only become evident when hundreds of thousands of people have taken a new medicine.

The safety of feverfew – the results of human studies

My colleagues and I have documented information from question-naires completed by more than 300 feverfew users, representing in excess of 600 patient years of daily treatment. This is probably more data than is available for some new medicines at the time application is made for a product licence and certainly more information than is available on most herbal products.

No major untoward effects attributable to feverfew were evident from this study, but it was not a clinical trial and users took different amounts of feverfew, so the data would be of limited value from a drug regulatory agency's viewpoint.

The safety of feverfew – blood tests in long-term users

Just as many illnesses cause changes in the cellular and chemical composition of blood, so can the toxic actions of drugs and chemicals. Blood tests are therefore of vital importance in patients receiving new drugs.

Some blood chemicals are present in different concentrations in women than men – blood fats for example – and some blood enzymes increase in concentration with age. For these reasons, it was not sufficient merely to test the blood of those taking feverfew, but also to control test for changes due to age, sex and migraine by examining blood samples from other people who were not eating the plant but who were the same age and sex. All participants were first examined to exclude other illness and tests were carried out on the following four groups of 30 individuals:

- migraine sufferers who had taken feverfew daily for more than three months, but preferably for more than a year
- migraine sufferers who used to take feverfew daily but who had stopped taking it at least three months before the tests were done
- migraine sufferers who had never taken feverfew
- healthy volunteers who had never suffered from migraine and neither had they ever taken feverfew.

The blood of each of these 120 people was tested for 40 separate constituents. Although a few abnormal values were obtained, the four groups did not differ in any significant respect, so no evidence emerged that implicated feverfew in causing damage to any vital organ. The same conclusion was reached in a comparison of the blood biochemistry and haematology of two groups of migraine patients – long-term feverfew users (average use 2.9 years) and never-users, 30 in each group – in a study published in *Human Toxicology* in 1987 and 1988 (see below). Just one element (erythrocyte sedimentation rate – ESR – the rate at which the red blood cells separate from the plasma, a high figure perhaps pointing to a health problem if there are also other symptoms and signs) was slightly higher in the group of feverfew users, but this was not considered to be clinically significant. Similarly, the use of feverfew in the double-blind clinical trials mentioned in Chapter 3 was not associated with changes in the chemical or cellular elements of blood and urine when compared with the test results of those people taking the placebo.

In my opinion, the amount of safety data obtained from these studies more than equalled that expected on completion of phase 1 of the clinical evaluation of a new drug in man, the main difficulty being how to assess the effect the variation in the daily amount of feverfew being consumed might or might not have.

The effect of feverfew on human chromosomes

As we have seen, feverfew is rich in chemicals known as sesquiterpene lactones, principally parthenolide, which has been shown to cause cell damage (cytotoxicity) *in vitro* (see Chapter 7). Consequently it seemed possible that these sesquiterpene lactones might be capable of inducing changes in the chromosomes or cause changes in other human cells in the individuals who had taken feverfew for long periods. In the mid 1980s, therefore, studies were undertaken by staff of the City of London Migraine Clinic in conjunction with members of the Genetic and Reproductive Toxicology and Cell Biology Department of the British Industrial Biological Research Association (BIBRA), Carshalton, to determine the frequency of chromosomal aberrations and other changes in the lymphocytes (white blood cells) of 30 migraine sufferers who had taken feverfew leaves, tablets or capsules daily for an average of 2.9 years compared with those of 30 migraine sufferers who had not taken feverfew. All 60 patients were women. The mutagenicity of urine was also determined for ten people from each group by means of a test to demonstrate the ability of the urine to alter the chromosomes of bacteria. The average daily consumption of feverfew was the equivalent of 73 mg of dried leaves.

The results of these studies (published in *Human Toxology*, 1987, vol. 6, pp. 533–534, and 1988, vol. 7, pp. 145–152) indicated that the chromosomes of circulating lymphocytes taken from migraine-sufferers who had consumed feverfew daily for prolonged periods were not significantly different from those of matched controls who had never taken feverfew in terms of the incidence of abnormalities. These results were also supported by the finding that there was no increased mutagenicity of the urine of the feverfew users compared to the non-users.

In this study, care was taken to exclude smokers, people recently exposed to X-rays or viral diseases. The two groups were also controlled by matching them for age, alcohol and caffeine consumption, all of which can affect the chromosomes. The sensitive tests used would have picked up, for example, increased concentrations of mutagens in the urine of cigarette smokers.

The side-effects of feverfew

The assessment of the incidence and severity of side-effects caused by drug treatments is an important part of all clinical studies. Side-effects can be defined as those unwanted pharmacological actions of a medicine, occurring with doses normally used to treat a condition. Examples include drowsiness from tranquillizers such as diazepam (Valium), vomiting with the antimigraine drug ergotamine (Migril) and the dizziness experienced with some drugs that lower high blood pressure too quickly.

Minor side-effects experienced when taking feverfew were reported by only 17.9 per cent of the 270 people who responded to our questionnaire. The types of side-effects and the percentages of these people who suffered them were as follows:

- mouth ulcers/sore tongue – 6.4
- abdominal pain/indigestion – 3.9
- unpleasant taste – 3.0
- tingling sensation – 0.9
- urinary problems – 0.9
- headache – 0.9
- swollen lips/mouth – 0.4
- diarrhoea – 0.4.

Exactly 66 per cent of all those who remembered when their side-effects began said that they were apparent within the first week of treatment. Curiously, when those suffering from migraine only were asked for the same information, 66 per cent of them said that their side-effects came on gradually over the first two months and only 25 per cent of them experienced these side-effects in the first week of treatment.

When feverfew users were asked whether or not they had ever experienced specific side-effects, such as ulceration of the mouth or indigestion, while taking the leaves, a higher proportion of them said that they had than when they were just asked whether or not they had

had any side-effects. For example, 11.3 per cent said that they had suffered from mouth ulcers and 6.5 per cent experienced indigestion compared with figures of 6.4 per cent and 3.9 per cent for these side-effects when they were just asked about side-effects generally.

No serious side-effects were reported in the two double-blind clinical trials of feverfew as a treatment for migraine discussed in Chapter 3. Both studies found minor side-effects, the most frequent of which in the Nottingham study was mouth ulcers, which occurred more commonly among those being given the placebo treatment than those receiving feverfew. This illustrates how important placebo-controlled studies are for distinguishing genuine side-effects from the chance occurrence of ailments that are, in fact, unrelated to the treatment. However, it must be borne in mind that the clinical trials undertaken so far have been of relatively short duration whereas many of those who responded to the questionnaires had been taking feverfew for some time. Longer treatment periods might have led to a higher incidence of side-effects.

Mouth ulcers

Some people are known to have more sensitive skin than others, and they can get a rash when their skin comes into contact with certain plants, such as the primula. Contact dermatitis, as it is called, has also been reported with feverfew. Those who react in this way also have cross-sensitivities, reacting to other plants related to feverfew, such as asters, chrysanthemums, ragweed and tansy. Florists are particularly at risk of having contact dermatitis caused by these plants. Also, some people are allergic to certain foods such as plums and strawberries, and come out in a rash when they eat them. We were interested to know, therefore, whether the mouth ulcers occurred because of a contact dermatitis-type reaction as a result of chewing the leaves or a reaction of the body to the substances absorbed from the leaves.

Users of raw feverfew leaves had always assumed that the mouth ulcers they got were a contact dermatitis-type response but this was easily disproved. When I transferred a 39-year-old feverfew user from leaves to capsules containing dried feverfew, she still suffered from mouth ulcers. When, unknown to her, placebo capsules were substituted for her feverfew capsules, her ulcers cleared up within a week.

Some people who start to take feverfew capsules containing a high dose of the dried leaf (100 mg or over), obtained through the post or from healthfood shops, have written to the migraine charities to say that they get dreadful mouth ulcers. So, buyers beware! The feverfew capsules available at the time of writing have been marketed without adequate clinical testing to support the dose advocated on the packaging or its safety. There are at least two products that control the content of the most abundant substances in feverfew, but it is not known whether or not these are linked to the beneficial or unwanted effects of the plant.

Mouth ulcers are the most common troublesome side-effect attributed to feverfew and, from what we have seen, they most probably occur as a result of the actions of one or more substances absorbed from it after it has been eaten.

Some people think that because feverfew causes mouth ulcers it most probably causes stomach or intestinal ulcers as well. Certainly, aspirin-like drugs can do this and one of their more common side-effects is a slight blood loss from the site of ulceration. So, the possibility that feverfew might cause blood loss and hence lead to anaemia was something we looked for when we interviewed and examined feverfew users. Happily there is no suggestion so far that feverfew-induced ulceration of the mouth is accompanied by ulceration elsewhere in the body.

Of the three women I discovered to be anaemic on examination and who were subsequently confirmed to be anaemic by blood tests, one had an hereditary blood condition called thallassaemia, in which the red corpuscles are wrongly formed and break up, while the other two had chronic iron deficiency anaemia, which was most probably due to an inadequate intake of iron in the diet. In neither case was there a history of symptoms suggestive of ulceration of, or bleeding from, the alimentary tract.

Mouth ulcers are caused by other drugs, too, indeed they are commonly encountered with most of the drugs used in the treatment of rheumatoid arthritis – the anti-inflammatories, gold and penicill-amine. As in the case of feverfew, the ulceration is caused by these drugs after they have been absorbed from the intestine or site of injection. That feverfew induces mouth ulcers even when it is taken in remarkably low daily doses shows that the plant contains powerful substances that call for further detailed investigation.

Feverfew also sometimes results in a more widespread inflamma-tion of the lining of the mouth and surface of the tongue, often with swelling of the lips. This could be caused by the direct contact these parts of the mouth have with the plant during chewing. This side-effect tends to occur in susceptible people after several weeks or months of daily use, as this woman found:

A couple of years ago I ate two leaves every day and was delighted with the results. My headaches became very infrequent and I happily cultivated feverfew plants so that I was never without a supply.

However, after nine months of relative freedom from head-aches I stopped eating the leaves. I had side-effects which for me outweighed the advantages.

I lost all my sense of taste and my tongue developed deep fissures and a very ragged appearance. Possibly this is something peculiar to me . . .

Many of the people now using the plants I have passed on take their leaves as a drink or in a sandwich so that contact with the tongue is minimal and so far I haven't heard of any side-effects from them . . .

Reasons for stopping feverfew treatment

Virtually every domestic medical cabinet contains up to three prescription medicines that should have been taken as directed but were not, for a variety of reasons. Most people do not like taking medicines for long periods. They are suspicious of 'foreign' chemicals, of possible long-term effects, of lack of benefit or they may have experienced unacceptable side-effects. Thus it seemed advisable to find out why people stopped taking feverfew in order to see what side-effects were serious enough to lead to them giving it up.

At the time of our study, 164 users had stopped taking feverfew leaves. The principal reasons they gave for doing this were poor efficacy (30 per cent) or reasons unrelated to the plant as a medicine, such as the inability to obtain leaves (24 per cent), especially in winter. Anxiety over suggestions in the press of potential side-effects accounted for 10 per cent. Others stopped taking the leaves because their migraine improved, only to recur. In fact, only 20 per cent of those who stopped eating feverfew did so because of side-effects, the majority of which were to do with the gastrointestinal tract, such as mouth ulcers, heartburn or indigestion, nausea and/or vomiting. My advice is to stop taking feverfew at once if you experience any serious symptom. You should also consider stopping feverfew treatment if you have any mild symptom that doesn't clear up in three to four days while you are still taking the herb. If the problem does not disappear when you stop taking feverfew, inform your doctor.

If you think you may be allergic to feverfew but wish to take it, ask your doctor if you can have a patch test done (an extract of feverfew is applied to a small area of skin under a patch to see if there is any reaction).

Feverfew and other drugs

So far no clear-cut adverse interactions between feverfew and drugs used to treat additional medical conditions of migraine sufferers (see Chapter 3) have been found. However, it is reasonable to suppose that some of the medicines and painkillers, for example, would enhance the beneficial effects feverfew has on migraine.

That there was an absence of obvious unfavourable interactions between feverfew and a large number of diverse conventional drugs when taken simultaneously is encouraging. No adverse interactions have yet been recorded between feverfew and almost 50 different drugs and drug combinations used for the treatment or prevention of migraine. Nor does there seem to be any suggestion that feverfew is more likely to cause mouth ulcers or other side-effects when taken with other medicines. Naturally, however, it will be necessary to watch for potential interactions between feverfew and other drugs for a long time yet.

7

How does feverfew work?

Feverfew is related to the tansy, chrysanthemums and chamomiles, all of which contain volatile oils in hairs on the surface of the leaves. These oils include, among other chemicals, a class of substances known as the sesquiterpene lactones. In feverfew, the main one of these present is parthenolide. Many other chemicals in feverfew have been identified, such as camphor, steroids and flavonoids. As you can see, the chemical make-up of the plant is extremely complicated, with numerous classes of biologically active substances. Which of these make feverfew effective in combatting migraine remain unknown, but most researchers have concentrated their attentions on parthenolide – the most abundant 'plant metabolite' – and compounds related to it.

How exactly feverfew works is not completely understood. Parthenolide-like substances have a range of biological actions. They relax the smooth muscle of the hollow organs, such as the intestine, kill bacteria, lower blood fats, are anti-inflammatory and cytotoxic (they cause cell damage or death). Thus, in rats, they prevent arthritis and have some actions in common with the non-steroidal anti-inflammatory drugs (NSAIDs), preventing the migration of white blood cells to damaged tissue and the synthesis of prostaglandins. Some tumour cells isolated in the laboratory are irreversibly damaged when exposed to sesquiterpene lactones, the manufacture of RNA and protein being inhibited, but not that of DNA.

The suggestion (which amounts to conviction for some scientists) that parthenolide or other sesquiterpene lactones in feverfew are probably responsible for its effect in migraine stems from the observation that these agents (and crude feverfew extracts) reduced the secretory activity of blood platelets and white blood cells kept active *in vitro*. It is true that disturbance in the functioning of the platelets in the blood has been noted by those researching migraine and that platelet secretion occurs during a migraine attack, but very few scientists now regard this as having a causal link with migraine.

Although more laboratory experiments on feverfew extracts are undoubtedly necessary, it should be pointed out that they are no substitute for investigations into the effects of feverfew in man. For example, tests done on blood platelets in blood samples taken from long-term feverfew users react normally to a whole battery of substances that make them secrete their contents, which suggests that the irreversible effects observed on isolated healthy cells *in vitro* do not happen in actual feverfew users. If this is so, though, how can the 'platelet effect' of feverfew be responsible for its beneficial effect in preventing migraine?

The ability of feverfew extracts to inhibit the release of enzymes from granules within white blood cells inside the fluid of inflamed joints has been suggested as an explanation of how feverfew works to relieve symptoms of arthritis. Notwithstanding the fact that the only clinical trial so far carried out to investigate the effectiveness of feverfew as a treatment for arthritis did not show feverfew to be of benefit, for such a mechanism to be involved would mean that parthenolide or some other sesquiterpene lactone would have to be absorbed into the blood and be transferred via the circulation to the joint fluid. How likely is this to be the case?

Let us take as our starting point the standardized 125 mg tablet of feverfew containing 0.2 per cent (that is 0.25 mg) of parthenolide. If we assume that parthenolide is completely absorbed and escapes being broken down by the liver – and this is unlikely – then one quarter of one milligram will be diluted in a blood volume of approximately 3 litres (about $5\frac{1}{4}$ pints) to give a concentration of about 80 nanograms in each millilitre of plasma (that is, 0.00008 milligrams per millilitre of plasma). However, few drugs that are taken stay only in the blood, and for parthenolide to be able to be present in joint fluid, it must be absorbed into the other bodily fluids apart from the blood, the volume of which is about 16 litres (about 28 pints). So, if parthenolide is eventually evenly distributed throughout this fluid, its concentration in each millilitre would be around 16 nanograms. However, it is highly likely that a chemical like parthenolide would also find its way inside the body's cells, which, naturally, would lower its concentration in the tissues even more. The question remaining is whether such low concentrations of parthenolide could act in the same way in the body as high concentrations did *in vitro*.

In my own studies on isolated tissues, parthenolide did not have an effect on muscle stimulants when it was used in concentrations of less than 10 micrograms per millilitre, which are more than 100 times higher than the highest plasma concentration that could be achieved in theory and more than 600 times the theoretical maximal concentration achievable in joint fluid after a person has taken a single 125-mg standardized tablet. Even allowing for the possibility of there being an accumulation of the substances when someone has been taking tablets regularly and for them to increase the number of tablets they take, the difference between *in vivo* and *in vitro* concentrations would still be very wide. Other researchers have had to use even higher parthenolide and other feverfew extract concentrations than I have in their *in vitro* experiments on blood and muscle cells in order to see effects, all of which makes it most improbable that the effects of the chemicals in feverfew that we have looked at so far are likely to explain why feverfew can help people with migraine. Indeed, if the published irreversible effects of feverfew extracts obtained *in vitro* on the blood cells and muscles of blood vessels, intestine and other hollow organs were to occur in man, they would probably be toxic and cause serious side-effects. Those who have taken feverfew know this is not the case, which suggests that the body might be able to alter the chemicals in feverfew, such as parthenolide, to render them safe. There are theoretical grounds for suggesting that some of the normal blood chemicals, cysteine for example, may neutralize the activity of the sesquiterpene lactones after they have been absorbed.

Opposite effects have been obtained with extracts of dried feverfew that do not contain significant amounts of parthenolide and related chemicals. Scientists at King's College, London, and Nottingham University have recently shown that the muscle of blood vessels is contracted (shortened) by these extracts possibly because they interfere with potassium passing across the muscle cell membrane. They postulated that this contracting effect – which ergotamine (Migril) and sumatriptan (Imigran) also cause – might explain how feverfew can relieve migraine symptoms. However, three observations argue against accepting this as an explanation. First, feverfew acts as a preventive and is not used for the treatment of acute migraine episodes, unlike ergotamine and sumatriptan. Second, again, extremely high concentrations were needed to produce this effect *in vitro*, concentrations that would not be achieved in real people. Third, both fresh feverfew containing parthenolide and dried feverfew products appear to work in migraine (although it is true that only dried feverfew products have been used in clinical trials). The contraction effect produced by this newly reported component of dried feverfew would, presumably, be blocked irreversibly by the parthenolide and other sesquiterpene lactones occurring in fresh feverfew.

So, under what circumstances might the chemical substances in feverfew exert their effects in human beings? It is possible that a particular organ, part of the brain for example, could be concentrating the chemical(s) – indeed this is known to happen with some medicines. Alternatively, the substance in feverfew that works to prevent migraine might not become biologically active until its structure has been chemically modified by the liver, in which case it would resemble certain pro-drugs, which only work when they are changed in the body from an inactive to an active state. Finally, it may be that animal tissues have a lower sensitivity to the feverfew chemicals than do human tissues. The human blood platelet studies make this third explanation most unlikely, however.

So, despite some 20 years of research, how precisely feverfew works is still unknown.

8

The safe way with feverfew – the dos and don'ts

The majority of herbal 'medicines' are readily available. Although they are promoted as medicinal, they make no specific claims for effectiveness in disease and therefore do not come under the Medicines Act. Thus, consumers are left largely unprotected, particularly from those unlicensed remedies, the standards of which may be extremely variable.

The variability of the content of feverfew tablets and capsules has been recognized and attempts have been made to standardize feverfew products. One such has been granted a drug identification number by Canada's Health Protection Branch, allowing the manufacturer to make the claim that, even though it is a non-prescription drug, it is effective in the prevention of migraine. The Canadian authorities have set a recommended daily intake of 125mg. However, the vast majority of feverfew products bought by the public are not standardized and no product has yet been approved by the UK Committee on Safety of Medicines. One of the notes for guidance issued by the European Community's Committee for Proprietary Medicinal Products concerning the quality of herbal remedies lays down quality standards for the description of the particulars of the constituents; the methods of preparation; control of starting materials; control tests during the manufacture of the finished product; control tests on the finished product and stability tests.

Does natural imply safe?

Feverfew users start taking the plant believing rather than knowing it to be safe, and it comes as a surprise that side-effects sometimes occur. Yet, less than half a century ago, many drug treatments used to be obtained from plants and these plants – or chemicals and extracts derived from them – were used to treat disease in exactly the same way that many synthetic chemicals are used today. Thus, just as the synthetic chemical is defined as a drug when used as a

76

treatment, so is a medicinal plant when it is used as a treatment, and we have ample evidence in the case of feverfew that this includes a plant's ability to induce side-effects.

It is sometimes claimed that plants and their extracts are less toxic than synthetic compounds simply because they are 'natural', as though this bestows on them a property of safety not enjoyed by synthetic drugs. In fact, as we have seen with feverfew, plants and plant extracts are simply large collections of chemicals – mini drug producers. These chemicals are just as likely as their synthetic counterparts to cause toxic effects. Indeed, some plant chemicals are highly poisonous – curare, hyoscine, muscarine, nicotine and strychnine being well-known examples.

It may be that as more is learned of feverfew, the phenomenon of synergism – where the effect of the whole plant or a crude extract has a stronger or better tolerated effect than one isolated, pure constituent – may be demonstrated, but there is no evidence for this at the moment. On the other hand, it might be argued that to give an unknown but large number of foreign chemicals is likely to place a greater stress on the body's metabolic processes than would a single chemical the effect of which had already been identified in animal studies. It could also be argued, as I have done, that the variable constituents of the leaf from plant to plant and season to season might make for an unstable dosing regimen that would be likely to cause problems.

No drug has yet been invented that will not have a damaging effect somewhere in the body if the dose is high enough. Thus we can say that all drugs are toxic when more than the recommended dose is taken. In the case of feverfew what constitutes a toxic dose has not been determined. We know from the herbals that up to 140 times the dose people take each day today was taken for some conditions and it had little more than a purging effect, but then the writers of the herbals might have been reluctant to report their failures.

As Dr R. G. Penn, Principal Medical Officer at the UK Department of Health, wrote in the October 1983 issue of the *Adverse Drug Reactions Bulletin*:

The belief that herbal medicines are non-toxic may be badly mistaken, and it is unsafe to rely on the observations and conclusions of patients and physicians of the distant past who would almost certainly have overlooked such subtle toxicities as carcinogenicity, mutagenicity, and hepatotoxicity even though they have recognized more obvious acute adverse effects. Regrettably, there have been few scientific studies of the efficacy and toxicity of herbal medicines, and most of the relevant reports are of the uncontrolled 'clinical impression' type.

The average consumer may well not be aware of what sorts of controls are really needed prior to the manufacture of a plant product. Plants are grown in soil and are therefore likely to be contaminated by harmful bacteria, the presence of which must be tested for. If pesticides have been used, their residues and those of fumigation agents and toxic metals derived from soil and air must be detected. If plant extracts are used, then there must be accurate tests to identify these, their purity and the characteristics of their constituents. If, as is the case with certain feverfew products, the product is standardized with regard to the presence of constituent chemicals believed to have beneficial effects in a disease, then how that standardization is achieved must be specified. Furthermore, when plants are grown and harvested commercially, contamination in the form of toxic weeds must be controlled for. Only the more reputable companies are likely to set up such quality control procedures.

The need for education on herbal products

There is a definite need for high-quality information on herbal products. Shops selling herbal products tend to have promotional material available that highlights the favourable and minimizes the hazardous features of these products. Education about the potential risks as well as advantages to health of herbal remedies is essential and it should be presented in a balanced manner.

In 1993, Dr D. V. C. Awang, Head of the Natural Products Bureau of Drug Research, Canadian Health Protection Board (HPB), identified the misinformation about feverfew then in circulation, (*Herbalgram* 29, page 34). Ironically, as we saw earlier, the HPB has approved a 125-mg leaf product of authenticated feverfew (*Tanacetum parthenium*) containing at least 0.2 per cent parthenolide. This figure for the content was apparently arrived at by means of a mathematical extrapolation of the parthenolide content of feverfew used in the two British clinical trials outlined in Chapter 3. In granting this licence, the assumption appears to have been that parthenolide is the principal active ingredient of the leaves that works to prevent migraine. The truth is, however, as we have seen, that what it is in feverfew that has this effect is unknown. The fact that parthenolide and other feverfew extracts inhibit the reaction of blood platelets *in vitro* to a variety of stimulants but that platelets taken from long-term feverfew users react normally to these same substances, strongly suggests that such tests are irrelevant to what actually happens when feverfew is taken by migraine sufferers and/ or that parthenolide and related compounds in their unchanged form may not be responsible for the beneficial effects migraine sufferers experience. If the latter is true, then if tablets or capsules of pure parthenolide were taken they should not prevent migraine. I understand that such a clinical trial on parthenolide may be in progress. The importance of standardizing the parthenolide content of feverfew products, in my view, is as a means of limiting the amount of potentially dangerous substances they contain and that patients ingest until the active substance in feverfew has been identified.

So, if you are inclined to try feverfew or another herbal product do be careful. The daily dose of feverfew recommended by manufacturers varies from 25 to 1200 mg compared to the dose of 50 mg used in our clinical trial (for a list of some of the products, see Baldwin, *et al.*, 1987. *The Pharmaceutical Journal*). Just because they are available doesn't mean they have been tested for efficacy or safety in man or animals. This is nearly always the case if a clear medical use for the product is not stated on the label as you can be fairly sure that if any testing has been done, the manufacturer will mention it. The following dos and don'ts are suggested only as a guide to assist you in finding reliable feverfew or other herbal products.

*Dos**

- Only buy feverfew products from well-established, reliable retail outlets.
- Check that the packaging states which herbs have been used and which parts of the plant.
- Ask for the exact instructions/directions for use – how much to

take and how often. Never buy a product that does not give any directions for its use.

- Only buy authentic feverfew plants from a reliable supplier if you intend to grow your own.
- Keep feverfew products out of the reach of children.
- Store feverfew in a cool, dry, dark place.
- Only purchase feverfew products that have a use-by date on the pack.
- Consult your doctor if you have a serious illness or disease.
- Always tell your doctor or pharmacist you are taking feverfew.
- Stop taking feverfew if you experience severe side-effects or mild ones that do not clear up in three to four days and inform your doctor if these persist.
- Be cautious and stop taking feverfew at intervals to see if you still need it.
- Vegans should check any tablets or capsules as they may contain materials derived from animals.

*Don'ts**

- Don't buy feverfew products from overseas, especially by mail order, as you then have no idea as to the safety, or otherwise, of what you are buying.
- Never buy a product the composition of which is not detailed on the label.
- Never buy a feverfew product unless the manufacturer's name is printed on the label.
- Don't buy a feverfew product unless it is clearly labelled as being authenticated *Tanacetum parthenium.*
- Don't use feverfew products that you have kept for more than six months.
- Don't use feverfew for illnesses other than migraine.
- Never try feverfew for a serious illness such as cancer or jaundice – this is too risky.
- Don't eat any herb that you simply believe to be feverfew – you must be completely certain that it is feverfew.
- Don't exceed the stated dose of feverfew – if it doesn't work within three months, stop taking it.

* Adapted with permission from P. A. G. M. de Smet *Side-Effects of Drugs Annual*, M. N. G. Dukes and L. Beeley, (Eds), Elsevier Science, Amsterdam, 1990.

- Don't take feverfew if you are pregnant or breastfeeding.
- Don't take high doses, that is more than 125 mg daily of dried feverfew as tablets or capsules or five small raw leaves each day; the dose given in the clinical trial was about half this.
- Don't take feverfew if you know you are allergic, or your skin is sensitive, to contact with chrysanthemums or related plants.
- Don't take tablets or capsules containing another herb or chemical in addition to feverfew. There is no evidence for the safety or efficacy of combination products.
- Don't believe all of what you read about feverfew on the Internet. Much of what I have found there is factually wrong.

Where do we go from here?

From a regulatory standpoint, the situation for feverfew remains unsatisfactory. Further definitive, double-blind, placebo-controlled clinical trials need to be undertaken with groups of migraine sufferers receiving different 'doses' of standardized feverfew tablets or capsules so their efficacy and safety can be confirmed and the optimal dose can be defined to the satisfaction of all physicians. Thereafter, trials need to be undertaken to monitor those taking the optimal dose over longer periods so that at least 100 people eventually receive standardized feverfew for 12 months or more. Such a trial to monitor feverfew's safety is particularly important as feverfew contains potentially toxic substances. A clinical trial programme of this kind would take about five years to complete and be expensive but relatively straightforward to undertake. A major difficulty that might be encountered might be that of controlling the quality of the manufacturing process, ensuring that the tablets or capsules are identical in composition from batch to batch.

The substance that has the beneficial effect need not be determined by such a trial. The disadvantage of not identifying it, however, is that toxic compounds that are unnecessary to achieve the beneficial effect would possibly continue to be ingested. Indeed, ineffective but toxic compounds might wrongly be thought to be useful. Nevertheless, assuming that all the quality issues can be resolved, a feverfew product that had been so tested and found to be safe could be granted marketing authorization.

Another way of taking feverfew from being a herbal 'remedy' to a licensed pharmaceutical product is to identify and develop its active constituent(s). A great deal has been discovered over the past decade in terms of identifying many of the chemicals in feverfew. Each of these would have to be isolated from the plant or synthesized in a pure form and then, after completion of the appropriate safety tests (Chapter 6), given to healthy human volunteers. The appearance of both the unchanged and altered chemical in the blood should be followed and any symptoms or effects on body chemistry recorded.

Take parthenolide, for example. A low dose of pure parthenolide – one similar to the amount in a 125-mg standardized feverfew tablet – could be swallowed in a capsule and blood samples taken at intervals in the course of 24 hours. If unchanged parthenolide, say, were to appear in the blood, then this would mean that it must have passed across the wall of the alimentary tract. That it had been absorbed would be an important first step in determining whether or not parthenolide could be regarded as a possible active constituent, which might then be worth testing in migraine sufferers. However, if neither unchanged parthenolide nor altered parthenolide were to be detected in the blood stream, then it would be less likely that parthenolide would be considered a potential migraine preventive, but a more detailed evaluation would need to be made in other phase 1 studies before it could be eliminated.

After passing this first hurdle in healthy volunteers, parthenolide would need to be tested extensively in phase 2 clinical trials, as described in Chapter 6. In the event that it proved to have no effect, then the whole process would have to be repeated with another feverfew constituent and so on. Thus, the conventional drug development process when applied to plant extracts is a lengthy, costly and high-risk one in which few drug companies would be prepared to invest. It is tempting to suggest, though, that those companies now profiting from selling unlicensed feverfew products should be encouraged to pay for this work to be done.

In conclusion

Feverfew is a promising plant medicine for the prevention of migraine, but before it can be used routinely for this purpose further assessments of its long-term efficacy and safety are needed. In particular, the dose must be defined, based on the identification of what the active ingredient of feverfew is. Until then, feverfew is likely to continue to be considered as an alternative remedy for those sufferers who are unable to tolerate orthodox drugs for migraine.

Further reading

Migraine and arthritis

Blau, J. N. (ed.), *Migraine*. Chapman & Hall Medical, London, 1987.

Dyson, S. *Coping with Migraine*. Sheldon Press, London, 1991.

Scott, J. T. (ed.), *Copeman's Textbook of Rheumatic Diseases*. 6th edition, Churchill Livingstone, Edinburgh, 1986.

Wilkinson, M., *Living with Migraine*. Heineman Health Books, London, 1976.

Feverfew products, doses and administration: information and misinformation

Awang, D. V. C. 'Feverfew fever – a headache for the consumer', *Herbalgram* 29, 1993, pp. 3–36.

Baldwin, C. A., Anderson, L. A. and Phillipson, J. D. 'What pharmacists should know about feverfew', *The Pharmaceutical Journal* 239, 1987, pp. 237–238.

Berry, M. 'Feverfew', *The Pharmaceutical Journal* 253, 1994, pp. 806–808.

Groenewegen, W. A., Knight, D. W. and Heptinstall, S., 'Progress in the Medicinal Chemistry of the Herb Feverfew', in Ellis, G. P. and Luscombe, D. K. (eds) *Progress in Medicinal Chemistry* 29, Elsevier Science Publishers B.V., 1992, pp. 217–238.

Lord, T. (ed.) *The RHS Plant Finder*. Royal Horticultural Society, London, 1996.

Clinical trials of feverfew

Anderson, D., Jenkinson, P. C., Dewdney, R. S., Blowers, S. D., Johnson, E. S., and Kadam N. P., 'Chromosomal aberrations and sister chromatid exchanges in lymphocytes and urine mutagenicity of migraine patients: a comparison of chronic feverfew users and matched non-users', *Human Toxicology* 7, 1988, pp. 145–152.

Hylands, P. J., Hylands, D. M. and Johnson, E. S. 'Feverfew in migraine therapy and research', in Blau, J. N. (ed.), *Migraine*. Chapman & Hall Medical, London, 1987, pp. 543–549.

Johnson, E. S., Kadam, N. P., Hylands, D. M. and Hylands, P. J. 'Efficacy of feverfew as prophylactic treatment of migraine', *British Medical Journal*, 291, 1985, pp. 569–573.

Johnson, E. S., Kadam, N. P., Anderson, D., Jenkinson, P. C., Dewdney, R. S. and Blowers, S. D. 'Investigation of possible genotoxic effects of feverfew in migraine patients', *Human Toxicology* 6, 1987, pp. 533–534.

Murphy, J. J., Heptinstall, S. and Mitchell, J. R. A. 'Randomised double-blind placebo-controlled trial of feverfew in migraine prevention', *Lancet*, 23 July 1988, pp. 189–192.

Pattrick, M., Green, S., Heptinstall, S. and Doherty, M. 'Feverfew in rheumatoid arthritis: a double-blind placebo-controlled study', *British Journal of Rheumatology*, 27, Abstract 233, Supplement 2, 1988.

Index